# HITOPADESH

*Didactic and interesting stories which transformed
the foolish princes into capable administrators*

*Worded by*
**'Kunwar' Anil Kumar**

## Manoj Publications

© *All Rights Reserved*

*Publishers*

**Manoj Publications**
761, Main Road, Burari, Delhi-110084
Ph: 27611349, 27611116, Fax : 27611546
Mobile : 9868112194
E-mail : info@manojpublications.com
*Website : www.manojpublications.com*

*Showroom :*

**Manoj Publications**
1583-84, Dariba Kalan, Chandni Chowk, Delhi-6
Phone : 23262174, 23268216, Mobile : 9818753569

ISBN : 978-81-8133-483-1

Price : 80/-

**Seventh Edition :** 2010

*Printers*
**Jai Maya Offset**
Jhilmil Industrial Area, Delhi-110095

**Hitopdesh :** 'Kunwar' Anil Kumar

# Contents

*Story behind Hitopadesh*                                  5

---

**THE ADVANTAGE OF HAVING A FRIEND**                      9

---

1.  Greed makes one blind                                10
2.  Think before you act                                 15
3.  With whom to make friends                            28
4.  The cunning cat                                      33
5.  Who was wiser                                        44
6.  who knows the future                                 49
7.  True friend                                          53
8.  Consequence of greed                                 55
9.  The elephant and the jackal                          58

---

**SUHRIDBHED**                                           66

---

1.  The cunning Jackals                                  67
2.  Naughty monkey                                       70
3.  Unnecessary concern                                  72
4.  A cat's fallacy                                      78
5.  The mystery of the bell                              84
6.  As you sow, so you will reap                         89
7.  Crookedness                                          95
8.  Solution to a problem                                97
9.  Using one's wits                                     99
10. When the sea was vanquished                         105

**VIGRAHA**      **113**

1. Once there was a heron      114
2. Foolish monkeys      116
3. The donkey in the guise of a lion      119
4. A ruse      121
5. Avoid the company of the wicked ones      126
6. Bad company yields bad results      129
7. False praise      131
8. Greedy barber      141

**SANDHI**      **145**

1. Compromise      146
2. Foolish turtle      148
3. Right decision at the right moment      149
4. Craftiness of a woman      151
5. Fault of a heron      154
6. Bad end      158
7. The sanctimonious heron      160
8. A poor Brahmin's dream      162
9. Two demons      165
10. An innocent Brahmin      168
11. End of a poor camel      170
12. A cunning serpent      173

# STORY BEHIND HITOPADESHA

Patliputra, situated on the holy bank of river Mandakini, has had a distinct place in history. This city, today, is known as Patna, and is the capital of Bihar. Earlier also Patilputra was a capital of a big state. And it was the kingdom of King Sudarshana, who was extremely powerful, scholarly and valiant. Chosen men of erudition from all over the country enjoyed a special status at the court of King Sudarshana. The king would offer appropriate veneration to scholars, and they, in return, would impart scholarly teachings and offer knowledge of prudence to him.

One day court proceedings were going on at the court of King Sudarshana. There was a discourse on prudence and knowledge by scholars in its full swing, and they were being rewarded suitably. During the discourse a scholar read a stanza—

**Anek Sanshayochhedi Paroksharthasya Darshanam.**
**Sarvasya Lochanan Shastran Yasya Nastyandh Ev Sah..**
**Youvanan Dhansampattih Prabhutvamvivekita.**
**Aekaikamapthanarthay Kimu Yatra Chatushtayam..**

Which would mean—'one can see across the mist of complications of religion and politics, society and history, through the eyes of knowledge only. Knowledge is such light that can put an end to all kinds of darkness in the world. It is not possible for human eyes to reach where the light of knowledge can. Great are the eyes of knowledge which can see what is not before eyes. Those, who do not have eyes of knowledge, are blind despite having eyes.

A person who acquires any one of—Youth, Wealth, Power and Glory—may commit the greatest sin, blinded by his ego. And what to talk of a person who acquires all the four?

**"Markatasya Surapanan Tato Vrishchikdanshanan,**
**Tanmadhye Bhoot Sancharo Yadva Tadva Bhavishyati."**

The King was greatly worried about his foolish sons after hearing these stanzas. All the sons of the King were foolish, dissolute, and voluptuary. Instead of being in the company of Pandits and scholars, they used to pass their time with people of low thinking, and, with the result, their level of thinking had also gone down.

King Sudarshana had such a big treasure that it would have been sufficient for seven generations, what to talk of one generation; but a person without knowledge is incomplete. What will be the fate of that country, the king of which, who bears the burden of all his subjects on his shoulders, who has to perform the great duty of running the whole country, is a fool? This was the problem which worried the king continuously. Day and night he would contemplate—'what is the use of having such useless and stupid sons?' He would think—'They have no interest in studies, nor do they think about religion; they are not aware of their duties. It is better not to have than having such sons.'.

Having no son, or even if the son dies just after taking birth, bothers a person for a short time; but having a son, who is imbecile, who keeps himself at a distance from religion and knowledge, who is not interested in studies, becomes a cause of permanent distress. Seeing such sons before eyes keeps their parents writhing in agony, and a day comes when they become the cause of their doom. Such sons, not only for their own selves, but also for the earth, are mere burdens. One son in enough if he is virtuous and gentle. A big number of unfiliual sons are as useless as the number of countless stars in the sky, whereas one worthy son is enough to bring splendour to his lineage.

'But none of the princes deserves to be called a worthy son'—sucked into the vortex of such thoughts King Sudarshana began feelings giddy, and at last he decided to make his sons more prudent and knowledgeable than himself at any cost.

The very next day, he called for a meeting in which he invited all the scholars and Pundits of other states apart from the scholars and Pundits of Patliputra. Welcoming them all King Sudarshana said—

"My respected fellow scholars! I have invited you all today because I am extremely sad-stricken for the fact that my sons have deviated from the correct path. Seeing my dissolute sons sends me worrying about the future of my subjects, and a question arises in my mind as to who will be their well-wisher after me. Having been enlightened by you all, I have arrived at the conclusion that I should solicit your advice in order to be able to bring an end to this darkness. It is you all who have taught me that only that person is considered wise who at the time of difficulty, consults other men of wisdom. So please advise me the method that I should adopt to bring my sons to the correct path."

One of those scholars was a great Pundit, philosopher, and intellectual Shri Vishnu Sharma. Hearing the King he rose from his place and spoke in a very humble and friendly manner—"My Lord! Why do you worry when I am here? I shall take your sons with me and get them out of the darkness of foolishness, and bring them on the path of wisdom with the power of the science of ethics. Perform your duties towards your kingdom and leave the rest to me. It is true, hard work brings result only where it is required. Learning also has its effect only on those who possess intelligence. Teaching a duck a hundred times won't enable it to cram like parrots. Likewise, a fool also cannot be taught. But your sons are princes who have taken birth in a royal family. You yourself are an erudite scholar, and such scholars cannot beget foolish sons. The only difference is that your sons have not had proper education and the result is that they have deviated from the correct path. But now I shall take them with me. I promise that I shall teach them the science of ethics in such a manner that they will become great Pundits within a period of six months."

Hearing the great scholar—Vishnu Sharma—King Sudarshana became very happy. His consolatory words brought great relief to him. King Sudarshana handed over his sons to Vishnu Sharma and said, "Pundit Ji! You are the guardian of my sons from today. Having handed over my sons to you for learning the science of ethics, I have become free from all kinds of worries."

"Thank you, My Lord! I promise I shall carry out my duty with all my sincerity."

Saying this Vishnu Sharma went away with all the princes.

Pundit Vishnu Sharma observed the princes for a few days and then arrived at a conclusion that the princes were intelligent; it was only their bad company that had made them arrogant...'So, if I try to teach them straightaway, they will either leave this place and go away from here, or they will revolt against me.' Thinking thus, he thought of a new way to correct them so that they could gain knowledge and have entertainment as well.

Pundit Ji called the princes near him and said with great affection, "Look children! Wise people spend their time in study and gaining knowledge, whereas unwise ones waste their time in sleeping and quarrelling. So, for the sake of your entertainment, I shall tell you some very good stories, which will not only entertain you, but will give knowledge also. These will be very strange stories; the characters of which will be lions, tigers, deer, crows, turtles, and pigeons etc."

"Such stories will indeed be very interesting, sir," said the princes happily, "we shall love hearing such stories."

"Yes, do listen—First of all, my advice is that one should not be greedy. A greedy person risks his life just as the hungry pigeons had done."

"How so, sir?"

"Listen!"

The stories Pundit Vishnu Sharma told them on ethics were—

# THE ADVANTAGE OF HAVING A FRIEND

A friend is he who advises suitably and correctly. A friend is he who does not quit under adverse circumstances. A friend is he who ignores the greatest folly of his friend and sings his simplest virtues tirelessly.

It's difficult to get such friends. One should always be in search of such friends. Getting a true friend is an invaluable achievement in life. Are you a true friend?

# 1

# GREED MAKES ONE BLIND

On the bank of river Godavari, there was a huge silk-cotton tree. It had thick and shadowy branches. Years after years, it witnessed many passers-by who came, quenched their thirst, took rest in the refreshing shadow of it, and went away; but that silk-cotton tree maintained its existence in the same place.

The passers-by used to enjoy cool breeze in its shadow, and a variety of birds had made their nests on the thick branches of this tree and lived there. One of them was a crow—Laghupatnak—who also lived with his family.

Laghupatnak was elderly and experienced.

He used to keep an eye on everything all around.

Just by the side of the silk-cotton tree there was also a mango tree. This tree used to be laden with lots of mangoes during summer season. The passers-by were greatly benefited by these two trees. They would get sweet mangoes to eat, refreshing water from the river, and last of all, the shadow of the thick branches of these trees used to render great comfort to them.

Whenever there was storm, the passers-by would take shelter under these trees and enjoy the taste of mangoes that fell due to storm.

The crow, being the chief of his family, used to take full care of the whole family.

Often fowlers would be roaming around with their trammels in that area, due to fear of which the birds would be hiding in trees.

It was only the crow who was very watchful of his surrounding and also used to alert the other birds against any danger.

Once a fowler happened to come towards that tree.

Seeing the ripe mangoes his mouth began watering.

When he saw so many birds sitting in that tree, he laughed and said to himself—"That's great! I must consider myself lucky today. I shall enjoy the taste of these juicy mangoes and shall be able to trap these birds also."

Extremely pleased with the hope of getting a lot of birds in his trammel, the fowler scattered grains of rice in the field and setting his trammel he went and sat on the raised ground of the bank of the river waiting for the birds to get into his trap.

Just then a flock of pigeons came flying with their king—Chitragreev—and landed near the river to drink water from it. The fowler's mouth watered to see such a big flock of pigeons coming down.

The pigeons became very happy to see grains of rice scattered around and began saying, "Good Lord! We are so lucky today! We shall have sufficient food to eat and cool water to drink today."

Seeing the flock rushing to peck at the grains of rice, their king, Chitragreev said, "Hey, hey! Where are you all going?"

"Lord! We shall quench our thirst by drinking the water of this river, and then, you may see for yourself that lots of grains of rice are scattered here all around; we shall appease our hunger with it; and the most interesting thing is that you have your great *friend, Laghupatnak,—the crow—who lives in this silk-cotton tree. And thus, we shall have, not one, but three things accomplished today at a time.

"Oh, now I understand! It is the greed for the grains of rice that has made you all land here," said Chitragreev.

"Yes, Lord! You know already that we haven't eaten anything since morning; and you have always said that one who is hungry can't even pray to God wholeheartedly," said one of the pigeons.

"Look, my friend!" said Chitragreev, "Don't forget one thing—greed may sometimes cost you your life. The grains of rice scattered in this manner is only an allurement and is certainly a device of a fowler to trap us. I am confident that some fowler is sitting somewhere with his trammel set to trap us all."

"It is better to die with our hunger assuaged than to die of starvation," said all the pigeons in unison.

"Look, my friends! I am your king, and it is my duty to alert you of any danger ahead; but I am pained to realize that all of you are blinded by the greed of the grains of rice scattered around. Now this is for the last time that I am telling you that if you don't listen to me, you shall have to face the consequences, the like of which a passer-by had to face trapped in a swamp due to his greed for a piece of bangle," said Chitragreev, "and ultimately lost his life."

"How so?" the pigeons looked at their king anxiously.

On this, the story narrated by the king of pigeons was thus—

❏ ❏

# 2

# THINK BEFORE YOU ACT

Chitragreev, the king of pigeons, sat in the courtyard of the house of the crow, Laghupatnak. The pigeons were eagerly awaiting the story to be told by their king about the greedy passer-by who got himself caught in the swamp.

"My friends! I know it very well that all of you are eager to listen to the story of the old lion and the greedy passer-by; and moreover, you have before you the scattered grains of rice causing among you an allurement to assuage your hunger. But, first I shall tell you about the lion who, due to being old, could not find a prey for himself. And how could he, since he had become physically infirm and had lost many of his teeth? And helpless under these circumstance, he would be sitting by a lake, remembering his good old days, waiting for a prey to come to him so that he could easily kill and eat it.

"Though he had become old, he had never felt a decrease in his appetite. Being a lion, he could not eat someone else's kill, nor could he ask anyone to find a prey for him to assuage his hunger. Though there were thousands of kinds of fruit in the forest, eating which one could survive, the problem with the lion was that he was carnivorous and could eat flesh only.

"The lion would keep thinking—'how youth is important for any creature on the earth. One can never imagine during his young age the kind of problems he may have to face when he becomes old. It is only when one starts facing he problems of the old age that he is reminded of his good old days. And remembering the good old days is more painful.' These were the kinds of thoughts that would bother him most. Now his one last hope was God. From morning till evening he would keep praying—'O God! Now please send some creature or I would die of starvation.'

"One day, as soon as he opened his eyes after offering his prayers to God, he saw a golden bangle lying before him. He became extremely happy to see it and began making plans sitting by the side of the lake. The idea behind his plans was to assuage his hunger somehow. He was thinking of different ways to trap a greedy person and make a prey of him.

"Now seeing anyone passing by, he would say, "Brother! If, by any chance, you have dropped your golden bangle, you can come and collect it from me. It is here."

"But no fool would stop to collect the golden bangle, seeing it in the hands of a lion. He would know that the lion would kill and eat him instead of giving the golden bangle to him. He would think—'why should a lion give a golden bangle to someone? No matter how truthful and honest a lion may become, but will always remain untrustworthy.'

HITOPADESHA—1

"Many days passed thus. The lion would come and sit by the lake everyday, hoping that he might get a prey some day. The bangle was only an allurement to get some human being in his trap—otherwise he was somehow managing with some birds and small creatures; but this was not enough to satiate him. He needed a sumptuous one.

"Thinking thus, the old lion would continue sitting by the lake waiting for some greedy person to get into his allurement and fall in his trap.

"And one day—

One handsome boy came wandering toward the lake. The lion's mouth watered to see a boy of robust personality. "Aha! What nice flesh! O God! Please get him in my trap. I won't have to eat birds and small creatures for a few days at least," thought the lion.

"He began remembering his youth when he used to be able to kill and eat such preys at ease. 'But this old age! Oh God! How helpless I have become.'

"Meanwhile, the young boy came closer. The lion became alert. He said, "Brother! Perhaps this golden bangle is yours which you dropped here unmindfully. You may please take it back."

"The young boy looked at the glittering golden bangle and his greed for it got the better of him. He began thinking that it would be real fun if he could get it in his possession. But when he looked at the lion, he thought—'this lion won't spare my life. Lions and men can never be friends. But this lion himself is calling me and telling me to take away the golden bangle if that is mine...It is not proper to kick away the fortune when it is coming by itself. But I must take at least some risk. People go to far off places to earn money; and I am getting it at a very close distance from my house. If I sell this golden bangle, I shall be able to do some business in my village itself, and run my family. Moreover, this lion is very old. Killing me is beyond his capability.'

"Greed makes one go blind. He forgot that a lion was after all a lion; be it old or young. He went to the lion and displaying great affection he said, "O the king of the forest! You indeed are very pious. Otherwise no one returns someone's golden bangle these days. This deed of yours will become a matter of pride for all the lions. But I am a little reluctant in coming to you."

"Innocent boy! I understand your predicament. We have a bad name among you human beings. But human beings are least to be blamed. It is in fact us lions who have committed so many atrocities on you human beings. And I am one of them. But, believe me! I have changed myself totally and taken a pledge that I wouldn't participate in any of the sinful acts. I shall not kill any human being and shall lead the rest of my life in observing penance and austerity. I shall be praying to God all the time. I am aware that it was because of my sinful acts that my wife died when I was very young. And the result is that I am wandering all alone at this age. I am so unfortunate that even the god of death is not kind enough to take me away from this place. How to tell you my friend, how sad I am! If you can believe me, the truth is that I had come to this lake to commit suicide, but a gentleman like you stopped me from doing this, and said commiting suicide is the greatest of all the sins. He said that it is better to say goodbye to your sinful life and lead a virtuous life than committing suicide. And this will bring a happy end to your life. It is since then that I have changed myself completely and taken a firm decision that I won't kill a human being any more. And this is the reason why I remain sitting here. Just see how much I have changed. Seeing this golden bangle I thought that you might have dropped it inadvertently, and so why not return it to you. Once a sage had told me that in the Shastras (religious scriptures) there are eight paths to religion—

1. Yajna (religious sacrifices on the altars), 2. Self-study, 3. Charity, 4. Austerity, 5. Truthfulness, 6. Patience, 7. Forgiveness and 8. Contentment.

"Of these eight paths one may observe Yajna, Self-study, Charity and Austerity sanctimoniously, but the last four—Truthfulness, Patience, Forgiveness and Contentment are observed by sages only. Now you may see for yourself, there is nothing like greed in me, or else, who is there one earth who would return the gold found lying by him."

The young man was greatly impressed by the lion. He said, "O king of the forest! I am fed up of my poverty..."

"I could guess so the moment I saw your face. Even if this golden bangle is not yours I would very much like to give it to you; because I know it's no use giving it to a rich man. It has been said to Yudhishthira in the Mahabharata—'You are respected by the charity made by you to the poor. Giving to the rich is useless. A medicine is supposed to act on a patient only. What is the use of giving medicine to someone who is not suffering from illness? In the same manner, money benefits only those who are poor.' In our Shastras, a charity is considered meaningful only when it is made by one's own hands. This precisely is the reason why I wish to give this golden bangle to you with my own hands, and thus atone for my sins."

"Now the young boy was fully convinced that whatever the lion was saying was in the interests of the young boy. He did not even remember that friendship between a lion and a human being is like friendship between fire and water. But avarice is such a thing that it may make a person jump into the fire also.

"He had forgotten everything. The glitter of gold had made him go blind. He had taken the lion to be a virtuous one, whereas the lion was feeling happy to see the young boy getting into his trap. He was successful in his first move, and now he was contemplating his next move.

"O king of the forest! Give it to me. Please give this golden bangle to me," said the greedy young boy.

"Yes, yes, I shall definitely give it to you. I have no hesitation in giving it to you in charity. But, first you take bath in this lake and purify yourself, and only then I shall be able to accomplish the act of making charity.

"The young boy took off his clothes immediately and jumped into the lake to take bath. The poor young boy didn't know that he was going to be caught in the swamp. He was caught in the swamp as soon as he took the dive and went on going deep into it. He tried his level best but could not come out of it.

"O friend! It seems you are caught in the swamp," said the lion.

"Yes, O king of the forest! I am badly caught in it. Now only you can take me out of it," said the young boy nervously.

"Yes, yes, I shall definitely get you out," saying this the lion got into the water carefully. The young boy noticed that the lion's countenance had changed; his eyes had become red. It took him no time to realize that he was fully in the trap of the lion. The lion was approaching with his real instincts. He had realized that the lion had used the golden bangle as an allurement to get him into his trap and had succeeded in his move. Something the lion could not accomplish with his physical power, he succeeded in accomplishing it using his wits and cunningness. The scholars have correctly said that one should not, even by mistake, rely on the current of water, someone armed with weapons, an animal having claws, an animal having horns, a woman and a king's clan.

"It has also been said that one should be judged by one's nature, and not by his virtues, because it is the combination of virtues that forms nature. For example—moon in the sky provides cooling effect to the people on the earth; it symbolizes beauty, but sometimes Rahu (one of the nine principal planets), casting its black shadow on the moon, makes it look ugly.

"It is impossible to avert what one is destined to. The intentions of the lion had become absolutely clear to the young boy beyond doubts. And when one is face to face with death one starts realizing one's follies. He knew it only too well that he was in the trap of the lion and also that it was too late to repent.

"And within moments his throat was in the jaws of the old lion and his sharp teeth had begun penetrating his soft flesh. He screamed with pain and everything was over. The birds around flew away to hear his pitiable scream."

The king of pigeons, Chitragreev, finished his story and looking at his friends said—

"Friends! Never do anything without contemplating it; because a good harvest, a son who is an erudite scholar, a good wife, a wise king, anything said having considered its pros and cons, and anything done under proper mental functioning never give bad results."

"The pigeons were compelled to rethink their decision about the scattered grains of rice when they heard their king speaking so eruditely. One of the pigeons who was very conceited about himself spoke with haughtiness, 'All what you say is bookish and rubbish; things change with time. Everyone is not necessarily a cheat. Some scholars have even gone to the extent of saying that the wise and the old should be listened to only during the periods of emergency. If we keep fearing all the time, a day will come when we shall die of starvation. One cannot assuage one's hunger without courage and efforts. There is nothing on earth free from doubt. It's only a matter of attitude. We have to change our attitude, or else, we won't be able to survive.'

"Yes, yes, what he says is correct," said all the pigeons in unison.

"The king of the pigeons began thinking—'Anyone can understand that it is impossible for deer, made of gold, to take birth. But still a personality like Lord Rama believed this impossible truth and ran after it because he was compelled by Sita Ji. Lord Rama himself was beguiled and it was so only because a person is blinded when he has his bad time ahead.'

"Now it became clear to the king of pigeons, Chitragreev, that all his friends had come down to a revolt against him because of one foolish and greedy pigeon. It was meaningless to talk of wisdom and genuineness before them. He thought—"all my efforts are futile

21

because no matter what quantity of water is poured on a slippery stone, not a single drop of it will stay on it."

"All the pigeons swooped down on the scattered grains of rice, and its result was not hidden from the eyes of the king of pigeons."

"On the one hand the pigeons began pecking at the grains of rice and on the other hand the fowler pulled the string of the trammel.

"Seeing all the pigeons trapped in the trammel Chitragreev became extremely worried and said, "Friends! It's not your fault, and you should never forget that when the bad times are ahead, even friends seem enemies. Even something said genuinely or a friendly advice sounds ill. The conceited and naughty pigeon was only a pretext. Anyway whatever was preordained, has taken place. Now the primacy is of getting out of the situation. It's no use repenting the past. Past is like a pyre from where we can get ashes only. We have to look into the present which is standing before us in the form of death. Reprimanding our friend at this hour is meaningless. Scholars say that one, at the time of difficulty, must observe patience, call for a meeting and discuss the matter. One, after getting wealth, doesn't lose his mental equilibrium, one who doesn't lose heart when in difficulty, one who fights bravely in the war, is a rare person. Those who wish to become great and rise high must keep themselves away from vices. Remember, combination of small things make a big unit. For example, so many thin strings twisted together make a rope; and a rope can lift heavy burdens and tie an elephant also. There is great power in unity. What I mean to suggest is that all of you should start flying together so that you may fly away with the trammel."

"The scholarly discourse of Chitragreev was an eye-opener for the pigeons; they felt as if they had awakened from a deep sleep. A new energy began flowing in their bodies. The pigeons were filled with courage.

"They looked at each other and signalled something silently and said—

"There is great power in unity."

"Come on, friends! Let us apply all our energy together."

"We shall face whatever may the consequence be."

"Chitragreev, the king of pigeons said—'God helps those who help themselves. Even if we have to die, we must die fighting.'

"Right then, all the pigeons applied their energy, all at a time and began flying with the trammel. The fowler who was so happy to see so many pigeons trapped a moment ago, was virtually perplexed to see them flying in the sky along with his trammel.

"The fowler ran after them for quite some distance, but knowing that it was futile trying to chase them, he gave up. He began lamenting his ill fate.

"Not only did he lose the pigeons, he had lost his trammel also. He began thinking—'what would I do without a trammel?' The trammel was his only source of earning, and he had no money for a new trammel.

"The pigeons, who were flying along with the trammel, saw their king, Chitragreev, and Laghupatnak, the crow, following them. Seeing them coming behind, they were convinced that their king would somehow manage to save their lives. When they reached a certain place above a forest, Chitragreev called out—'Enough! Now please all of you land here.'

"All the pigeons came down. Laghupatnak and Chitragreev also landed there. Chitragreev said to them all, "Look! Please don't get nervous. I have a friend, Hiranyak, who is a mouse. He lives in a hole under this tree. I shall call him; he will gnaw at the strings of the trammel and free you all from the trap."

"Chitragreev went near the hole in which his friend lived and called out—"Friend, Hiranyak! Please come out."

"No brother! I shall not come out unless I am fully convinced about your identity," said the mouse, "and I say this because you are not alone; there are so many with you, and I don't trust the outsiders."

"Fear not, O friend! One with me is not a stranger; he is my friend, Laghupatnak. My friends are trapped in a trammel. Only you can rescue them."

"All right! I am coming out if that is the problem. It is my duty to rescue someone if he is in difficulty," saying this Hiranyak came out of the hole.

"Coming out of the hole and seeing the pigeons caught in a trammel, Hiranyak understood that they had fallen prey to their greed. Just then Chitragreev came forward and said, "Look, dear! These are all my friends who, because of their hunger, have been trapped in this trammel. They have used all their energy and courage to reach this place. Now only you can save their lives."

"Friend! Everything is clear to me now. A friend in need is a friend indeed. Please don't worry! I shall cut the strings of the trammel with my sharp teeth right now and free them all," saying this Hiranyak began nibbling at the trammel.

"The pigeons were extremely happy to be freed from the trammel. Hiranyak had kindly rescued them and given them new life. The conceited and haughty pigeon bowed before Chitragreev and said, "King! Please forgive me. It was in fact because of my stupidity that all these friends of mine had reached in the mouth of sure death. We all would have lost our lives, had your friends, Laghupatnak and Hiranyak, not rescued us."

"All right! Don't worry! Let us forget the past and begin a new life. Scholars have said—

"Save money to save yourself from crisis. A woman needs more security than your money; but considering yourself above money and women, it is necessary for you to think of your own security first. Remember! Everything is based on the security of your own life. If your life is secured everything is secured. Life is better than bags of gold."

"Hearing this the pigeon once again bowed before his king and said—

"King! You indeed are great! It was my false pride that I did not listen to my king. I had risked my life and risked the lives of my friends as well. You are after all my king, but these two friends of yours are indeed very nice. It is because of their kindness that we have been extended a new lease of life. Someone has correctly said—"a friend in need is a friend indeed."

"Look, this is my sincere advice to you to forget the past and lead a new life. But you shall have to take a pledge not to allow a recurrence of this kind in your life. Wise men forsake their houses and lives for others. Money and body both are liable to decay. Then why not make good and proper use of these. Something that is temporary and has no permanence, should be made proper use of. Not only this, you are a pigeon and I too am a pigeon in appearance. We look alike. But what is it that makes us different from each other? It is simply the wisdom that causes the difference. You all are my subjects, and I am your king. If I had wanted I would have left you all when you were trapped by the fowler. But I didn't act in this manner. It is a king's foremost duty to provide safety to his subjects. And I can even risk my life for the safety of my subjects."

"This is a new chapter of austerity and sacrifice. And what one gets in return is glory. One who gets glory gets everything in life. Whosoever it may be—what is his end?

Death, only death.

But we forget that our bodies are liable to decay, and our good deeds and virtues become immortal.

"Hiranyak, the mouse, became very happy to know the invaluable ideas and thoughts of his friend. And who would not be happy to have such a wise and thoughtful friend? He saluted his friend, Chitragreev, and said, "My friend! You are great. And it is the virtuous who become great. One must consider himself fortunate to have a friend like you. And so far as the mistake committed by these pigeons is concerned, you have said enough. Please put no more pressure on them. I know it was because of their foolishness that they got trapped; but we have to think why at all did they commit this mistake. Only because they were hungry. Hunger makes one mad. One may commit the greatest mistake if his stomach is empty. And then there is also the factor of the influence of the previous births on every creature. One has to reap the consequences of his deeds in one form or the other. Birds flying in the sky fall prey to some kind of problem or the other. Small fish in deep oceans fall prey to bigger fish. And under these circumstances who is there on earth who can tell good deeds from bad deeds. There is none who knows the future."

"Both friends were engaged in scholarly discourse for a long time. Then Hiranyak, the mouse, arranged food for everyone with the help of his friends. Chitragreev's friend, Laghupatnak, was greatly impressed by Hiranyak. He thought that it was rare to have such wise and true friends in the world. Only true friends come out with a helping hand when one is in a difficult situation. One who has good friends, can overcome lots of great problems in his life.

"But one, who has wicked, cunning and selfish friends, far from overcoming his problems, gets deeper into problems. They would always be waiting for their friends to get into some kind of problem so that they could show false sympathy to them and serve their ends. Since the crow was impressed by the wisdom of the mouse, he decided that he would make friends with him and consider himself lucky thus."

"And so, after everyone had finished meals, and it was time to say goodbye, Laghupatnak said to Hiranyak, "Look, dear Hiranyak! My name is Laghupatnak and I live in the nearby forest. I wish to make friends with you."

"Brother, Laghupatnak! What you say is correct. But how can we become friends! Crows are known for eating mice. This kind of relationship will never allow us to carry on our friendship. Moreover, I don't even know you."

"What difference does it make, my friend? I am a friend of your friend, Chitragreev."

"Look, friend! Those, who make friends with someone without considering all the vital points, are bound to repent like the deer whose life came to risk because of his friendship with a jackal."

"How so?" asked Laghupatnak.

"Listen! I shall tell you the story of that cunning jackal who brought the life of his friend, deer, in danger out of selfishness."

❏❏

# 3

# WITH WHOM TO MAKE FRIENDS

Long time ago there lived in a dense forest, two friends, a crow and a deer. They were such good friends that other animals and birds of the forest exemplified their friendship. While some others were of the view that friendship should be in one's own community, and having friendship with someone in another community doesn't bring good results.

But the crow and the deer, though listened to everyone, did only what suited them. The crow lived in a thick tree, and with him some other birds and animals lived in it. The deer had great affection for the crow's wife and his two young ones.

Once a jackal came wandering from some nearby forest. His mouth began watering to see a young and healthy deer grazing along the river side. He began thinking—"How tasty his flesh must be! His body is full of flesh. It would be real joy if once I get a chance to eat his flesh.' But then he again thought—"How can I eat his flesh. I am not strong enough to be able to kill a deer. After all I am simply a jackal. No, no, I shall not be able to kill such a big deer."

But a jackal's cunning brain works very fast. He knows how to make use of others to serve his own ends. From top to bottom he is an epitome of cunningness. He began contemplating knavery in planning out his stratagy to get to his prey. He decided to make friends with the deer first and thus get him in his clutches. He thought—"Others may call it cheating, but I shall call it tactics. If someone is incapable of achieving one's goal physically, there is no harm in using his wits and accomplishing his goal," thinking thus he went to the deer and said in a very sweet voice—

"Hello, brother!"

The deer looked at him and began thinking—

"Who this jackal is, and how does he know me?" Then he said, "I reciprocate, brother! But I am sorry, I don't even know you."

"Brother! How does it matter even if you don't know me? In fact the truth is that I am returning to this forest after very many years. My parents left this forest long back. Now since they are no more unfortunately, I am absolutely alone. I had no friend in that forest. And, under these circumstances, I decided to return to this forest hoping I might get some friend here. Coming here when I saw your innocent face with loving countenance, my heart said—'see you have got a lovely friend now. How simple and affectionate! A creature who doesn't think ill of others. One must make friends with such creatures only.' Tell me my friend—will you accept the friendship of a sad-stricken jackal?"

The deer continued looking at the sad face of the jackal for quite some time. The innocent deer was not aware that the cunning jackal, who was talking to him so sweetly, was in fact making plans to get him in his trap under the pretext of friendship. In fact the deer was very simple and knew nothing of cunningness. So, he said to the jackal, "Brother, Jackal! Don't worry if you don't have a friend. You may take me as your friend from today. You don't have to worry about anything so long as I am here."

The jackal was extremely pleased to hear this, and, sitting on the cushion of soft and green grass, he began talking very sweetly to the deer.

Gradually it became time for the sun to set. All the animals of the forest began returning. The deer also prepared to return and said to the jackal, "All right, brother, jackal! I am preparing to return; you must also return now. It is getting dark."

"But, brother! I have no place where I can take shelter in this forest," said the jackal displaying great innocence, "why don't you allow me also to go along with you. I too shall get some place for shelter near your home."

"Brother, jackal! What you say is correct, but, just think, who would allow a stranger to stay around him. Circumstances are such that no one trusts anyone. Then how would someone trust a stranger? Who knows what he has in his heart?"

"Brother, deer! What is this you are talking about?" said the cunning jackal with greater sweetness in his voice, "On the one hand you have accepted me as your friend and on the other you call me a stranger. Dear Brother! How can I be termed a stranger, once you have accepted me as your friend? If someone asks you about me you can tell him that I am your friend. And that will be enough for me. Rest I shall take care of."

"All right, brother! Let us go. How does it bother me!" said the deer in all his simplicity.

When the deer and the jackal reached near the tree in which the crow, his friend, lived, he was questioned by the crow—"Dear friend! who is this creature with you?"

"An outsider. He has none in this world," said the deer.

"And it seems you have made friends with him," said the crow.

"What could I do, friend? His sad story made me feel pity on him," the deer said.

The crow said to the deer in a soft tone, "Look, friend! One should not make friends with just any stranger. The scholars also advise not to make friends with strangers about whose lineage you know nothing. Let me tell you that for one such mistake an old vulture had to take the severest punishment because of the crime committed by a cat. That innocent vulture had to lose his life."

"What are you saying, dear friend?"

"Whatever I am saying is in your favour; and remember, those who talk very sweetly are generally big cheats."

"And why did the vulture have to die? What had the cat done? Who was that cat?" the deer asked the crow.

"Yes, I shall tell you the story first and then leave it to you to decide about it," said the crow. Slowly he began telling the story of the cat and the vulture.

❏ ❏

# 4

# THE CUNNING CAT

A very long time ago, there lived many families of various kinds of birds in a very big banyan tree on the bank of a river. Birds of different communities had made their habitats in the tree and living together had created a great bond of love among them for each other. Be it a happy or a sad occasion they participated invariably.

There also lived an old vulture in the same tree. He had none left in his family and was leading an isolated life. Since he had become old and grown physically infirm, he could not make much movement. He used to sit alone in the tree and shed tears remembering the days of his youth. The other birds living in the tree pitied him and had full sympathy for him. And because he was old he was respected a lot by all the birds. All the birds took out a little of whatever food they brought and gave it to the old vulture to eat. Thus, the old vulture used to get sumptuous and sufficient quantity of food to eat.

The birds used to call him Tau Ji (father's elder brother). They used to go to the old vulture and offer their salutes to him every morning and evening. They would say, "Tau Ji! There isn't anything that you have to worry about so long as we exist. Don't consider yourself alone either. After all we all are yours."

One day all the birds called for a meeting, and in the meeting it was decided that since all the birds go away to collect food early in the morning and the young ones were left uncared for everyday, it will be Tau Ji who would look after the young ones in their absence. And we can have no better custodian than him. In return we shall take every care of him.

The resolution was passed unanimously in the meeting and the old vulture had nothing left to worry about concerning his future. Now he had only one job in his share, and that was taking care of the young ones of all the birds living in the tree. Now the birds had no worries about the safety of their young ones. Both the parties were happy. The old vulture began passing his time happily, and there wasn't anything that could bother him any more. The young ones of the birds would play all the time with the grand old vulture, and thus solve his problem of isolation.

One day a cat came wandering about under the tree and his mouth began watering to see so many young birds in it. He began climbing the tree.

The old vulture saw an unknown cat trying to climb the tree. This made him furious. He said angrily, "Who is it climbing the tree without permission?"

The cat saw a vulture sitting on a branch of the tree. He realized that a vulture being a ferocious bird it was impossible for him to succeed in his mission. He began thinking—"What to do now?" Then he remembered what his scholarly friend used to say—

"Fear not till the object of fear comes before you. One, who, instead of getting frightened, tries to elude the cause of fear, is considered wise."

The cat thought—"It's impossible to run away from the vulture, and also, running away will spoil my game; so, let happen whatever I am destined to, but I shall have to be a little diplomatic if at all I have to survive and succeed in my plan. Sometimes, things that may not be accomplished through physical power, can be managed diplomatically. And thinking this, the cat went straight to the vulture and spoke in a very humble manner, "Tau ji! Please accept my salutes."

"Who are you?" asked the vulture in a loud tone.

"I am a cat."

"Cat...? what brings you here? What purpose do you want to serve in our habitat?" The vulture's anger was growing every moment. He looked somewhat alert also.

"Tau Ji! What makes you so angry? Look, the scholars say that a creature should not be hated, simply because he belongs to another community. Whether the creature is good or bad, should be judged from his behaviour only," said the cat in a very sweet voice.

"First you tell me your purpose that you want to serve in our habitat," said the vulture still maintaining his loud tone.

"Look, sir! I live on the bank of the river nearby and am a devotee of Lord Shiva. I pass all my time in the worship of Lord Shiva. I am not a carnivorous any more. I had heard a lot about your virtuous self from the other animals and birds of the forest; and so, I came to pay a visit to you. But I fail to understand why you suddenly became so angry to see me, whereas I was almost dying to see you at least once in my life time. I have heard that you have quit the path of violence and taken over responsibility of the safety of the chicks. I am your guest, and the

35

wise ones welcome their guests. Some scholar has said that it is the duty of the host to welcome his guest even if the guest is his enemy. Have you not seen that trees render their shade even to woodcutters who ultimately fell them. If the host cannot offer his guest anything to eat, at least he can talk to him sweetly. The scholars also say that even if someone of a low caste comes to someone's house, it is his duty to welcome him and extend hospitality."

The cat's scholarly discourse softened the vulture up to quite an extent and he began thinking—'This cat is very learned, but after all he is carnivorous,' and then he said, "Look, I have every respect for you, but you must understand my predicament—I owe the responsibility of the security of these chicks; how can I allow a predatory creature like you to come near me?"

"Tau Ji! I have already told you that I am a devotee of Lord Shiva now. I have stopped eating meat and I observe fast every Monday. Now why would I become a sinner by killing these innocent chicks? I can't even dream of any such thing. I would rather request you to kindly allow me to remain with you either as your friend or as your servant. I am like your son. I would like to pass the rest of my life at your service."

Hearing the cat speak thus the old vulture felt pity and permitted him to come and meet him whenever he liked.

What more could the cat have wanted? Poor old vulture was not aware of the machinations of the cat. He did not know that the heart of the wretched cat was full of sinful thoughts. Gradually the cat managed to win his faith. Having done this he came down to fulfilling his plan. Everyday he would manage to kill and eat at least one chick. The vulture never knew that the cat was betraying him.

The birds, finding their chicks missing, would weep, search around for them and then finally give up. They didn't know that there was an enemy visiting their habitat everyday and eating away their chicks.

Now the birds realized that their chicks were not safe in the tree. And in order to counter the problem they called for a meeting. A pigeon said, "Brothers! It's no use sitting and weeping. It would be rather more practical to search for our enemy."

Every bird obeyed the pigeon and they launched a massive search for the enemy. While they were combing the nearby places, they happened to see a big hole in the ground under the banyan tree. Some birds entered the hole and saw a heap of bones. "It must be the old vulture who is eating our chicks everyday," thought the birds.

The birds became very furious and attacked the vulture together. They said, "You cheat! You have betrayed us. You kept cheating us by eating away our chicks."

"Murderer...oppressor...!"

The vulture was not even given a chance to speak and prove himself innocent. And ultimately the innocent vulture had to lose his life. And the irony of his fate was that none of the birds cared to know the real truth. The cunning cat was watching the scene from a distance and sensing the danger ahead he fled the place.

As soon as the crow finished telling the story, the jackal became furious all of a sudden. He immediately asked—

"Did you know anything about the lineage of the deer the day you established your friendship with him? And if you cannot reply to my question, tell me how you two entered into such deep friendship with each other. Still you two are bosom friends."

Hearing all this the deer said, "Look brother! Let us forget our differences and live together; because there is great strength in unity. All of us are like members of one family on this earth. For example, this crow is my friend; likewise, you too may become my friend. Whenever someone is in difficulty it is his friend who comes forward to render his support. Just think—what do we get out of this kind of argument? First we have to realize that there is great strength in unity; because if we remain united, not even the most powerful of our enemies can defeat us. Victory comes to those who remain united."

By now it had become clear to the crow that the deer was in no mood to listen to his friendly advises; the wicked jackal had already taken him in his trap. Ultimately the crow gave in and agreed to it that the deer should make friends with the jackal.

Earlier they were two, and now they were three.

But the jackal had his own machinations. He was like a wolf in lamb's skin.

One day the sinful jackal hit upon a new idea. He came with a big smile to the deer. The deer asked, "Hello, friend! What is it that makes you so happy today?"

"Dear brother! One naturally feels delighted when one hits upon a new and a profitable idea."

"What new idea is it? Please tell me."

"Look, friend! There is a field nearby which is full of greenery. We shall have real joy eating there. Here you have to satisfy yourself with whatever dry grass you get to eat; but if you accompany me to the place I am talking about you will get food that you have never tasted before."

"If that is so, I am ready to accompany you. I too am fed up of the kind of grass that I have been eating all along. In fact I have always had a longing for such kind of delicious food, but I could never dare go out, as I never had a friend like you."

"Now you cannot say that you do not have a friend. Here I am to take you along."

"Yes, friend! Let us go. May God bless you. I am indeed very happy that there is someone who will help me fulfil my wishes."

The jackal was happy that he was successful in his plot, and the deer was happy because he was going to get good food. Both started off happily.

They crossed the forest and reached a lush green field full of millet. The deer became extremely happy to see such delicious food before his eyes.

"Friend! You have indeed brought me to heaven. Only very fortunate creatures can dream of such good food. I don't really know how to thank you."

"An elder brother doesn't have to be grateful to his younger brother for any kind of favour extended to him. It was my duty, and I have done it. Being at the service of the elder brother is a virtuous deed. Now eat your fill and I shall be on guard. You will get a signal from me as soon as I see someone coming this side."

The deer ate to his heart's content...and after he had his fill, they returned.

The deer was only too pleased. He had never had such pleasure before, in his life. Now it had become a routine for the deer. He would go to the field, across the forest, everyday in the night and enjoy eating millet, and return with the jackal before break of dawn. The deer had faith in him and thought that the jackal was his well-wisher; whereas the jackal's evil plans had sinister implications.

Two nights passed happily, but on the third night there was a trap laid for the jackal in the field. Unaware of the trap, the deer got himself caught into the trap. The deer called out his friend, jackal, for rescue.

Seeing the deer trapped, the jackal said, exhibiting false sympathy, "Brother! What is this? You have been snared by some sinner. Oh God! I could never imagine that you would be landing in this kind of trouble. Now, any moment, the owner of this field will come, cut you into pieces and throw away. Oh God! What to do now?"

But the jackal didn't mean what he was saying. In fact he was very happy from within. He was waiting for the moment when the owner of the field would come, cut the deer into pieces and throw away. And then the jackal would be the happiest being to devour the meat and relish its taste. He had succeeded in his plan, and so he began waiting for the owner of the field.

The deer trapped in the snare was begging earnestly, "Brother please save my life. You can very easily cut the guts of this snare," saying this the deer's eyes welled up with tears.

The jackal stood up and went near the deer with an exhibition of sincerity toward him. He tried to feel the guts with his teeth and suddenly retreated saying—"Brother! I am on fast today; I cannot cut these guts with my teeth. Yes, I can promise that as soon as the period of my fast is over, I shall free you from the trap."

But in his heart of hearts the jackal knew that the owner of the field would come early in the morning and kill and throw away the deer.

On the other side when the crow noticed that his friends, the deer and the jackal, had not returned, he flew to the field and saw the deer trapped in a snare, and the jackal sitting absolutely carefree. It took him no time to realize that there was something seriously wrong. He went near the deer and said, "Why, my dear! Ultimately my prediction has come true. I had warned you to be careful with this jackal."

"Yes, brother! I am hanging between life and death only because I did not heed your warning. And that wicked jackal is enjoying his time now."

"The jackal is not worried about you. He is, in fact, waiting for the owner of the field to come and kill you so that he could devour your flesh. Brother! I was aware that these jackals are never trustworthy. They belong to the species of snakes. No matter how much milk you feed them, but getting a chance they are sure to bite. One must keep away from such friends," saying this the crow took a long breath and said again, "This jackal is a cheat, a sinner. You will see, he will die a prematured death one day. Such selfish beings cheat others by talking sweetly. I shall pray to God to bring an end to the life of such a sinner. Look, my friend! Please don't repeat such mistake in future. Never make friends with such creatures who, getting an opportunity, would readily devour their friend's meat. Holding an ember is sure to burn your hand. How can such creatures be true friends?"

The crow was extremely sad-stricken. He was aware that the owner of the field would come any moment and cut the deer into pieces. He knew that the jackal was sure to succeed in his plans. He began thinking—'But this would be victory of a sinful act. The jackal, instead of getting punishment for sinning, would get the flesh of his friend to eat,' the crow was thinking thus when he saw the owner of the field coming. He said to the deer, "Look, brother! Your death in the form of the farmer is coming. The first thing he would do is to kill you as soon as he comes. Do one thing; inflate your stomach and pretend dead. He will think that not being able to bear the cold in the night you succumbed to death; and seeing you dead he will free you from his snare. And I shall signal to you by calling you when the farmer returns with the snare. Run away without looking behind as soon as you get my signal."

The deer obeyed his friend. He held his breath and inflated his stomach, and lay pretending dead. The farmer came near and seeing a dead deer in his snare, said, "This wicked creature has died ultimately. Everyday he used to come and graze my field."

He undid the trap and slung the snare over his back. No sooner had he turned back than the crow began shouting—

"Get up, my friend! Run!"

The deer stood up immediately and darted in the opposite direction. As soon as the farmer saw the deer running away, he began stamping his foot angrily and saying—

"O the wicked one! You cheat! On the one hand you have spoiled my crops and on the other you have run away deceptively. Wait! I am coming," saying this the farmer began chasing the deer with a staff in his hand.

The jackal realized that his plan had failed. Such great plan had yielded no results to him. He considered it wise to run away for safety of his own life; or else, the farmer might come and kill him in place of the deer.

Thinking this the jackal also began running away. Meanwhile, the farmer, applying his full strength, threw his staff at the deer, but by chance the staff came flying and hit the jackal instead of hitting the deer. The jackal died then and there.

Thus, ending the story the mouse said—"A sinner is punished by God in this world. God himself punishes the person who thinks bad of others. Some people are born sinners, and no one can change them. Those who are good will always do good deeds, and those who are bad, can never be expected to do good deeds."

Seeing him talk so wisely, Laghupatnak said happily, "You are indeed very scholarly. You have correctly said that one should never befriend someone who is fickle."

Hiranyak and Laghuptanak had a long talk on different spheres of ethics, and having understood each other correctly and realizing the mental harmony, they entered into a bond of deep friendship.

Both became very good friends. Chitragreeva went away towards his destination along with his friends. The crow used to keep flying in the sky and the mouse used to keep wandering about on the ground. The crow would always return with some fruit in the evening, and also if the mouse got something good to eat, would keep it safely for the crow to eat.

Both friends were passing their time happily thus, when their region was hit by famine. Everyone began starving and running away from that region. The mouse also said to the crow, "Brother! How long shall we starve here? We might get some way out if we abandon this place before we succumb to death."

The crow spoke in a sad tone, "But where shall we go? It's not easy leaving our home place and going away."

"But it's better to find a new place than dying of starvation in this region."

"I agree, but..." paused the crow for a moment and then said, "Friend! I know of a place where we may go and stay."

"Where is that place?"

"There is a pond in the nearby forest. Manthar, a turtle, who is a friend of mine lives in it. We too shall camp on the bank of it. What more do we need? This will help us get a good friend and we shall have a good time together."

X     X     X

Next day in the early morning both friends set out towards the pond. The turtle saw the crow coming. He became very happy. When the crow and the mouse arrived, the turtle welcomed them and asked for an introduction of the mouse.

"Dear friend!" said the crow, "This is my friend Hiranyak; a great guy. He is as good a friend of mine as you are. Dear Manthar! Please extend proper hospitality to him. He is very wise and scholarly."

"Bravo! My friend! You are very fortunate to have developed friendship with someone so nice. Someone has correctly said—It is only fortunate ones who get good friends. Now please tell me your purpose of visit."

"I shall tell you a story that will throw some light on the purpose of our visit," said Hiranyak. Manthar, the turtle, and Laghupatnak said in unison—"yes, yes! Please tell us the story."

❑ ❑

# 5

# WHO WAS WISER

Far away in the outskirts of a town there was a monastery where lived the Sanyasins.

The name of the head of the monastery was sage Bhangiri.

Bhangiri always considered food another form of God; and so, after having finished his meals, he used to tie the leftovers in a piece of cloth and hang it by the peg on the wall behind him.

I used to wander about in the monastery in search of food everyday.

One night I found out where he used to keep the leftovers after finishing his meals. And from that night I began managing my meals with the leftovers.

When the head of the monastery came to know that some mouse was eating away his leftovers, he brought a staff to kill me. The Sanyasin was now hell-bent to bring an end to my life. So, I became very alert. I made it a practice to come out in search of food only when the Sanyasin was deep asleep.

One day a friend of the Sanyasin came there to stay with him. A topic of debate arose between them as to who was more knowledgeable between the two. The head of the monastery was striking his staff against the floor again and again during the discussion. This he was doing to frighten me and keep me away from the food. But since the room was filled with the aroma of delicious food kept in the bag, I was finding myself incapable of checking my instincts.

"Look, friend!" said the head of the monastery, "A devotee of mine has given me sweets prepared with clarified butter. There is a mouse in this monastery who eats away all my leftovers everyday, and is wandering about now looking for an opportunity to eat away those sweets also."

"Friend!" said the other Sanyasin, "How can a mouse reach your bag of sweets which you have hung so high by the peg? There must be some secret in it. Listen, friend! When a young wife begins suddenly with display of all her love and affections for her old husband, one can easily attribute motives, and know for sure that there is some self-interest behind the exhibition of love and affection."

"How so? Please explain it to me."

"Listen! I shall tell you a story," saying this Bhangiri began narrating a story—

There lived a trader in a big city whose name was Lalchand. He had a lot of money and was very proud of it. He always used to say: There is great power in money. One can buy anything in the world if one has money.

And with the power of money he married a fifteen-year-old girl from a poor family. The name of the girl was Shanti. That innocent girl had no knowledge of worldly affairs. But growing with age she was learning things in her day-to-day life. Gradually she realized that her husband was of no match to her. For some time she tried to compromise with the unfortunate circumstances, but ultimately compelled by basic instincts she gave in.

There was a young and handsome servant in the mansion. His name was Sundar. Shanti, the wife of the trader, developed a liking for the servant which soon converted into an affair. She was so engrossed in his love that life became impossible for her without him. One day, sitting on a couch with Sundar, she was talking to him when suddenly her husband happened to come. She immediately ran toward him and hugged him in her arms. She said—

"Come, O my darling! Why do you go away leaving me alone? I can't live even for a single moment without you."

In fact Shanti was only fooling her husband by exhibiting extreme love for him. This made Lalchand, her husband, very happy. This was for the first time in his life that Shanti had shown such love for him.

"Darling! Get fresh! Meanwhile, I shall go and bring hot milk for you."

As soon as Lalchand went into the bathroom to get fresh, Shanti signalled to Sundar to escape from there.

Lalchand came out of the bathroom and Shanti gave him a glass of hot milk to drink. And she once again began enacting the same drama of love and affection. Lalchand was totally confused. He was not able to guess the reason behind such change in her.

Lalchand finished the milk and began responding to her actions and needs.

The maids of Shanti were watching all this from a distance. They were also surprised to see her behaving so differently with her husband. They became very curious and came to Shanti after Lalchand left. It took them no time to get the secret out of Shanti that she was in love with her servant.

On the next day the maids disclosed the secret of their love affair to Lalchand.

As soon as Lalchand came to know about the infidelity of his wife, he turned her out of his mansion. He said—

"You are an unchaste woman. You come from such a low class family that you don't deserve to become a member of a respectable family. Go and live in the house of some beggar, because you have come from the house of a beggar. Now get out of my house..."

"Gurudev!" said the friend of Bhangiri, "Now you yourself imagine! What was Lalchand so proud of? Why he didn't care for anyone? Why he didn't fear anyone? It was all because of his power of money. In my view this mouse also possesses something that makes him so fearless."

Gurudev fully agreed with the Sanyasin's views. At last they both decided to dig the hole of the mouse and take the hidden treasure out of it.

Finally both the Sanyasins managed to dig out my hidden treasure. Heartbroken I left the place in absolute disgust. Both the Sanyasins were very happy to get my hidden treasure, and I was shedding tears on my misfortune. Having lost my treasure I became so infirm physically that it was no more possible for me to take a leap and reach the bag full of tasty food. Someone has correctly said that money is behind all power. One who possesses money, has thousands of friends. A rich person is never criticized for anything; rather his vices are considered virtues. No matter how scholarly a person is, without money he bears no importance.

I thought about my problem for a long time and ultimately came to the conclusion that such persons who are greedy and have no control over their instincts, are always surrounded by problems.

Thinking thus, I took the path of sacrifice and came to this forest ultimately.

I consider myself very fortunate to have got a good friend like Laghupatnak and you too as a new friend.

Then Manthar, the turtle, said—"A person who accumulates money all his life forgetting all his genuine comforts, is like a donkey who dies carrying loads only. A miserly person is never able to make use of his money, and then how will anybody know how much money the miserly person has in his possession. When his money is stolen by someone or is lost somehow, he begins to suffer owing to the sadness caused by the loss. There is nothing wrong in accumulating money, but one who accumulates too much money has to undergo the circumstances a jackal had to."

"What had happened to the jackal?" asked Laghupatnak and Hiranyak.

The turtle began narrating the story—

❏ ❏

# 6

# WHO KNOWS THE FUTURE

Long time ago there lived a hunter named Bhairav in the village Kalyanakantak. One day he decided to go hunting. It had been for long that he had not eaten tasty meat. He also had on mind to sell the flesh of a deer and earn some money.

Thinking thus he went to a dense forest. There he saw a huge wild boar at a short distance. The hunter first thought of hunting the wild boar, but then thinking that the deer nearby would get alarmed and dart away, he decided to hunt the deer first. He poised his arrow on the bowstring and released it. Since he was a good marksman the arrow went straight and pierced the body of the deer. Next moment the deer was writhing lying in a pool of blood.

The hunter immediately lifted the dead deer, slung it over his back and proceeded in search of the wild boar which, seeing the hunter, had hid itself somewhere in the dense forest. Meanwhile, still searching for the wild boar he began making plans about his future. He began thinking that he would sell away complete flesh of the deer and keeping a little of the flesh of the wild boar he would sell away the remaining flesh of the wild boar also; and with the money earned from it he would get himself married.

Planning thus he came across a place from where he could see the wild boar clearly. He unloaded himself from the weight of the deer so that he could mark his target conveniently. He stepped forward, aimed at the wild boar and shot an arrow. The arrow found its mark deep in the flesh of the wild boar. The wounded boar turned back grunting and snorting and attacked the hunter angrily. The wild boar was bleeding profusely and wanted to exact one last revenge on the hunter before dying.

The wild boar, in one fell swoop, brought an end to the life of the hunter.

The hunter, who had always been hunting innocent creatures, himself became a target and lost his life.

The wild boar too was probably destined to kill the hunter as his last kill, because he too fell on the ground and died as soon as the hunter was killed. But, just as the wild boar was about to fall a snake had come out of its burrow, and the wild boar fell on it. The snake could not take the weight, and crushed under the huge body of the wild boar it succumbed to death. Now the scene was that there were lying four dead bodies under the tree, in the roots of which was the burrow of the snake.

It was mere coincidence that a jackal happened to arrive there wandering about in the dense forest. He was struck with astonishment to see four creatures lying dead under the tree, but at the same time he became very happy also.

"God! You are great!" muttered the jackal to himself, "Sometimes you make me starve for days together and sometimes you give me so much that it becomes difficult for me to decide as to what to eat and what to spare. Today is the most fortunate day of all my life. I shall be the happiest being on earth if all the days of my life pass in this manner. O God! I know not how to thank you! You have given me so much today

that even if I go on eating my fill for days together I shall have enough left for a number of days."

The jackal was extremely happy thanking God again and again. Now the problem before him was that there was such a big heap of food to assuage his hunger and he was not able to decide which one to start with first, and which one to save for future.

Lost in such thoughts the jackal decided that he would manage the first month by eating the flesh of the hunter. Then he would manage the next month eating the flesh of the wild boar and deer. And after he had finished eating their flesh he would start eating the flesh of the snake.

'But what to eat now'—was the question.

"Yes, what to eat now?" the jackal began thinking, and just then his eyes caught sight of the bow of the hunter. It's bowstring was made of gut. He thought—'For today I can manage by chewing the bowstring which is made of gut.'

Thinking thus the jackal began nibbling at the bowstring. Cut by the sharp teeth of the jackal the bowstring snapped, and with the result one end of the bow pierced the throat of the jackal with a violent jerk. The jackal also died on the spot. Now in place of four there were five dead bodies lying under the tree. Such are the consequences of avarice. How strange is it that one, who doesn't know what might happen next moment, wastes away his energy worrying for his coming one hundred years.

Thus, concluding the story, Manthar, the turtle, said—"What more to say my friends? I can only suggest to you two to stay with me and pass the rest of your life comfortably. It's with great difficulty that one comes across a true friend. We shall live together in this forest."

Hearing the turtle the crow said, "Friend! You are indeed very wise and scholarly. We shall never be able to forget your teachings."

❏ ❏

# 7

# TRUE FRIEND

One day the three friends having wandered around throughout the day were busy talking when a deer came there puffing and panting. One could clearly tell from his face that he was tired and frightened.

He hid himself behind the trunk of a tree. Manthar, the turtle, asked—"Brother! Why is it that you are so terribly frightened? Could we help you?"

"Brother! I am being chased by a hunter," said the deer trembling with fear, "it seems my last days have come."

"Friend! Have no fear! We are ready to help you in every manner possible. But please tell us what kind of hunter is he that you are so much scared," said the turtle assuringly and with great affection, "have no worries. We shall definitely find some way out for safety of our life."

"Friends! The king of Kalinga is going to declare a war on the neighbouring kingdom. He has camped with his army along the banks of the nearby river. Tomorrow morning they have planned to camp here. One of them was saying that they would be hunting wild game in this forest," and then as if about to burst into tears the deer said, "he also said that he would kill all the deers in this forest because he loves to eat deer's meat. It became clear to me that my days are numbered, and this is the reason why I have been running around for safety of my life. I am sure they will not spare the creatures living in this pond also. Such huge army is going to annihilate us for their food."

The description given by the deer frightened the turtle also. Overawed the turtle said, "Brother! If what you say is true, I too am going to make a escape from this place. Staying here would mean an invitation to death. Some people eat the flesh of turtles also with great relish."

"Yes, yes, friend! What you say is correct," said the mouse, "one should be always very alert when there are bad times ahead. Friends!

Manthar (the turtle) will save his life submerged under water, but what will happen to us creatures who live on land. We shall die a prematured death."

Just then the crow said, "O friend! Scholars say that water for creatures who live under water, fort for those who live in forts, forest for a lion who is used to living in the forests and ministers for kings have special importance."

The mouse said, "Friend! Your sermons remind me of a story which deals with the shock that a trader got to see his wife in the arms of a prince."

"And what's the story?" asked the turtle.

"All right I shall tell you the story now—

# 8

# CONSEQUENCE OF GREED

Veersen was considered the most powerful king of his time. After expanding his kingdom to a great measure the king appointed prince Tungabal the king of a province of his kingdom and sent him there.

The name of the province was Sitapuri.

After taking over the charge of Sitapuri province Prince Tungabal became a different person altogether. He had hardly entered the age of adolescence that he was declared king of a province; and this had filled him with great sense of vanity.

Once, when he was taking round of his town, he saw an extremely attractive woman standing on the roof of her house. Even the beauty of moon of full moon night could not match the beauty of that pretty woman. He kept staring at her for a long time.

He was lost in the thoughts of that beautiful woman even after he returned to his palace. In fact it was for the first time in his life that he had seen a woman of such peerless beauty.

Next day also while disposing of the royal matters at the court the beautiful appearance of that woman kept haunting the mind of Tungabal.

He began feeling that his life was incomplete without the beautiful woman he had seen the other day.

He called out to his maid who was very clever and asked her to find out every detail of that beautiful woman.

The clever maid immediately understood that King Tungabal had lost his heart to that beautiful woman and he wanted to satisfy his lust by getting her in his arms.

Scholars and great people follow correct path only till they are able to exercise control over their instincts.

Obeying her king the clever maid reached the house of that beautiful woman. She was wife of a trader and her name was Chanda.

Chanda was surprised to see the maid in her house.
She spoke with uncertainty—"you?"
"Yes, I."
"But who are you?"
"Whosoever I may be, but I am your wellwisher."
"You may be a wellwisher of mine, but I have neither seen you before nor do I know you."

"Your not knowing me doesn't mean that I too don't know you. And my master, King Tungabal, knows you better than I do."
"King Tungabal?" said Chanda nervously.
"Yes, my sister! You are fortunate indeed to have found favour in the eyes of the king. Lady luck has smiled on you."
"What are you saying?"

"I am telling you the truth."

"But I am not worthy of him."

"The decision has been taken by the king and I am under his orders to approach you with his message."

"But how would I reach him? Now it is for you to go and tell the king to find some way and compel my husband to send me to him."

The maid returned to the king and conveyed the message of Chanda to him. King Tungabal looked at the maid with surprise and said, "But how is it possible that a husband would send his wife to some other man?"

"My Lord! It's not difficult. There isn't anything impossible in this world. Scholars say that something that cannot be achieved through valiance, can be achieved through wisdom. Just as a jackal, applying his wits and wisdom, had succeeded in killing an elephant."

"How did he do that?" asked King Tungabal.

"My Lord! Scholars say that there is great power in wisdom."

"Tell me also about such wisdom," said the king to the maid.

The maid began narrating the story—

# 9

# THE ELEPHANT AND THE JACKAL

There lived a murderous elephant in the dense forests near Panchavati. All the animals except the lion in the forest feared him. The animals would start running in different directions for safety of their lives to see the elephant coming.

It is widely known about the jackals that they are very dastardly by nature. As soon as they heard about the entry of the murderous elephant into the forest, they convened a meeting among themselves. And an old jackal was appointed as their chief.

Putting the problem before his friends the old jackal said—-"Look, brothers! We are face to face with a great problem. We have been deprived of our sleep during the night because of the murderous elephant. I make a promise before you all that I shall not be at ease until I have killed the elephant with the power of my wits and wisdom."

"What are you saying, sir? Is it possible for an old jackal to kill an elephant?" said one of the jackals.

"Look, brothers! Neither I am afraid of that elephant nor have I learnt to fear. I don't even fear death. I don't care even if I have to sacrifice my life in trying to save the lives of my brethren. I once again repeat my promise and seek your co-operation in return."

"We are of course with you, but we shall always remain sorry for your death."

"Cowards! It's because of such creatures like you that the entire species of jackals has a bad name for dastardly nature. Now I shall change the history of our species. I shall prove that jackals are no cowards. If required we may challenge the might of an elephant also. Please don't worry about me. Just keep me in high spirits."

"All right, all right! We take pride in whatever you are going to do. We shall accept you as our chief if you succeed in killing the elephant, and shall celebrate your martyrdom if you are killed during the performance of such brave act. This will make our progeny remember you."

"All right! Let me proceed now," said the old jackal.

All the jackals encouraged their old leader and garlanding him with garlands of flowers they began shouting slogans of victory. Many other animals also of the forest collected there to see the procession of jackals. They had never witnessed such unity among jackals before.

The old jackal advanced fearlessly and approached the elephant sitting in a corner behind big trees. He offered his salutations to the elephant with reverence.

"Hello! Uncle, I am surprised to see you here," said the elephant.

"Just to see my king and know his well-being."

"Do you recognize me as your king?"

"You are of course our king. In fact a meeting of all the animals of the forest was convened yesterday, and all of them have sent me to you with a proposal."

"What is their proposal?"

"Actually all of us have begun to feel that there is no more a capable king in this forest. And so we wish to declare you our king, because you possess all the virtues of a worthy king. Scholars say that the first thing one should wish is a good king, then a good wife and then wealth. Because in the absence of a king who is there who would care for the safety of a wife and of wealth. Keeping this in view I have been sent to you. My only request is that you should give your acceptance to become our king, because there is none else to match your might and become our king."

The elephant became very happy. All the animals had declared him their king—there could not have been anything more pleasant than this proposal.

"My Lord!" said the jackal seeing the elephant silent.

"Yes."

"If you don't mind coming with me, I shall take you to those animals who are eagerly waiting to declare you their king. They have asked me to escort you to them so that they may enthrone you with the ceremony of coronation. There is not much of auspicious time left for this occasion."

The elephant had not even dreamt of becoming a king of the forest. He was extremely happy to hear the proposal of the old jackal. That foolish elephant immediately agreed to go with him. Lust power makes one go blind. The intoxication of power deprives a person of all his wisdom. He did not even consider it necessary to think why the jackal had come all the way and approached him to become their king.

The old jackal was happy that he was gradually becoming successful in his plan. The elephant was getting into his trap.

Both were moving happily. The old jackal had taken the route which was full of swamps. The elephant, blinded by the thought of becoming a king, didn't even notice the swamps in the way. And ultimately he was trapped in the swamps. He began looking around. He applied all his physical power to retreat but all in vain. He was not able to do anything. Nothing that could have got him out of the swamps.

Seeing the elephant caught in the swamps the jackal began laughing loudly.

"Thus, the clever jackal got the elephant into the clutches of death. All this became possible through wits and wisdom only," with this the maid concluded her story and looking at King Tungabal she said, "My Lord! The power of wisdom is neither in wealth nor in sword. You shall have to apply your wits and find some way to get your fiancee in your arms."

The suggestions given by the maid hit a responsive chord in the heart of the king. He kept thinking throughout the night as to what he should do to make things turn in his favour without causing unnecessary complications. He wanted to get the beautiful woman without letting it come to her husband's knowledge.

Ultimately he hit upon a bright idea. He planned to appoint the trader giving him some royal post at his court and thus lay his hand on his wife.

Next day he sent for the trader and appointed him at his court.

The trader became extremely happy to have been appointed at court which conferred on him the royal honour as well. The poor man did not even know that the king was serving his own ends in a very cunning manner.

Next day, King Tungabal called out to the trader and said, "Look, I am going to perform a new kind of worship from tomorrow. And for this new kind of worship I shall have to observe fasts for forty continuous days and every day I shall have to offer my worships to some pious woman. And because you are one of the honoured ones in the town, it will be possible for you only to bring one pious woman everyday."

"All right, my Lord! It will be my duty to bring one pious woman everyday till the fortieth day. You need not worry about it."

From the next day it became a routine that the trader would bring one pious woman everyday and after the rites were performed he would escort her to her house in the night.

King Tungabal really offered his worships to women brought by the trader and gave them expensive clothes and jewellery as gift while leaving.

Seeing all this, greed for such gifts got the better of him and the trader began thinking—"This king gives such expensive gifts to these women: if I bring my wife, she also will get just as expensive gifts. This is the best opportunity to earn a lot of money. After all the king is not going to treat her otherwise; he would only offer his worships to her." Thinking this the trader made his wife wear beautiful clothes and jewellery and brought her to the king next day.

King Tungabal had been waiting for this very day. It was for the trader's wife that he had enacted the drama.

Getting the beautiful woman, Chanda, in his room the king bolted the door from inside and hugged her impatiently.

Forgetting the worship they became busy otherwise.

The trader somehow became suspicious. He began thinking—"Why did the king bolt the door from inside today? He used to leave the door open while performing his worships on other days."

King Tungabal thought that the trader had gone already. But in fact the trader was peeping inside through a window.

The trader was terribly shocked to see the scene inside. He couldn't believe his eyes. He began castigating himself for having fallen prey to such greed that had brought such results.

But what could he do now? What is done cannot be undone. It was no use weeping and crying.

"O friends! This is how greedy people have to suffer. So you all too should keep away from greed and avarice as far as possible."

The didactic story was over and the turtle, leaving the pond in search of some other place where he could camp and remain secured, set out. Seeing the turtle going, Chitrang, the deer, Hiranyak, the mouse and Laghupatnak, the crow also began following him.

The turtle had hardly covered a little distance when a hunter happened to see him. The hunter picked him up and put him in a net. Chitrang, Hiranyak and Laghupatnak were shocked to see this.

Hiranyak, the mouse, began wailing and exclaimed, "We are so unfortunate that before we solve one problem, we are struck by another one." He said to his friends, "Friends! We shall have to do something to get our friend, Manthar, freed from the net of the hunter before he goes out of the forest."

"Yes, yes, we shall have to do something as soon as possible," said the other friends in unison.

"Listen!" said Hiranyak, "Chitrang should play dead near the river and Laghupatnak should pretend to be pecking at the dead body of Chitrang. Seeing a deer lying dead the hunter will definitely rush to the pond stimulated by the greed of deer's flesh. Meanwhile, I shall cut the gut of the net with my sharp teeth and free Manthar, the turtle. And when the hunter reaches near Chitrang, he should stand up and dart away."

The plan was agreed upon and everyone acted accordingly.

The hunter, thinking that the deer was dead, put his net under a tree in which Manthar was trapped and went near the pond. Meanwhile, Hiranyak freed Manthar from the net and Manthar immediately dived into the pond.

Seeing the hunter coming, Chitrang, the deer, stood up suddenly and darted in the opposite direction. Laghupatnak, the crow, flew and sat on a branch of a tree. When the hunter returned to the tree he found the turtle also missing. At this he became very sad and said, "Those who act without thinking like me have to face similar consequences. Someone has rightly said—"He who grasps all things will lose all," saying this the hunter returned cursing himself.

The four friends began living happily in that forest.

Hearing the stories the princes became very happy and said, "We are indeed very pleased to hear all the didactic stories from you." Vishnu Sharma blessed them and said, "May you all be successful in all your endeavours. Make friends with gentle ones, may your subjects be happy, may the king always follow the path of religion and may the earth be safe in the hands of the king. May your virtues be appreciated in a manner a youthful girl is appreciated and may Lord Shiva confer his blessings on you all."

❑ ❑

# SUHRIDBHED

'No one does good to anyone, everyone is concerned about oneself'—This is not only a doctrine but is a bitter truth. In order to make someone do something, it is necessary to make him realize how he would be benefited by doing that particular thing. And as soon as he realizes it he would be compelled to do it. This is the only way one can make someone do something for himself. This is a mantra which, if accomplished, will yield desired results.

# 1

# THE CUNNING JACKALS

Having finished one set of stories Vishnu Sharma began narrating another set of stories to the princes—

There lived Sanjeevaka (a bullock) and a lion in a forest near the river Champa. They were very friendly with each other. In fact the lion himself had befriended the bullock. The other animals in the forest were astonished to see such friendship among them. They considered this friendship unnatural.

Whatever may have been the reason, but the poor bullock had his own story. He was physically very infirm when he came to the forest. It seemed he was almost on the verge of death. He was not even able to move about. And it was because of his physical infirmity that his master had turned him out of his house.

In fact the bullock was young, but since his master used to load him beyond his physical capacity, he had become weak. Though his master had earned a lot of money using his labour, the day he noticed him displaying signs of weakness and infirmity, he turned him out without caring for him.

Ultimately he decided to take shelter in the forests. At least plenty of grass to assuage his hunger and plenty of water to quench his thirst were available there. And thus, he kept wandering about in the forests eating grass and drinking water from the river.

Fresh air, pure water, soft green grass, sleeping and wandering about with no work to do began showing its magic and Sanjeevaka began regaining his lost health.

Gradually he became very strong. Sanjeevaka, who once had become so infirm that he could not even move about at will, had become so strong that he would run miles and miles in the forest. Fatigue was something of the past now for him. He had become as strong as a lion.

One day while he was sitting and enjoying happily the cool breeze along the river bank, a lion happened to come there to quench his thirst. His name was Pingalak.

Just then the bullock bellowed with a loud sound almost like a clap of thunder.

The whole of the forest shook with the thunderous bellowing of the bullock. The lion had not been able to see him but was scared to death, thinking that some other very powerful lion had come to the forest.

The lion got so frightened that he did not drink water and hurried back to his den for safety of his life. Sitting in the den he began thinking about the strange problem.

At this hour of crisis he remembered his two attendants—Karatak and Damanak. These two were sons of a jackal who had been the

minister of the lion earlier. As soon as they entered the den, seeing his king sitting with a long face, they immediately understood that there was something wrong. "But what is the reason behind it?" they thought.

They of course knew that the lion had gone out to drink water. While going he was happy. Then why was it that he had become suddenly so sad? This was something they were not able to make out.

"My Lord! What is it that makes you look so sad?"

The lion had no reply. The thunderous bellowing sound was still reverberating around him. He was overpowered by the fear of the invisible and unknown problem.

Getting no reply from the lion, Kartak and Damanak went and sat at a distance and began discussing the issue.

"Brother Damanak!" said Karatak, "It is his problem. Let us not worry about it. These powerful ones never think about us. It is only us slaves who keep worrying about them."

Damanak said, "Friend! Never ever think in this manner; for if you serve your master loyally all your requirements and desires are sure to be fulfilled."

"What you say is correct," said Karatak, "but how are we concerned with all this? One who bothers oneself unnecessarily doing things that he ought not to do, kills himself like a monkey did while prying a wedge out of a log."

"How did that happen?" asked Damanak.

"Listen, I am going to narrate the story."

❑ ❑

# 2

# NAUGHTY MONKEY

Near Dharmaranya of Magadha a Kayastha named Shubhadatta was having a temple constructed.

Outside the temple some carpenters were engaged in sawing logs in order to make doors from them.

Meanwhile a group of monkeys happened to come there from a forest, wandering in search of food. They halted there to see a new building under construction.

All the monkeys entered the half-constructed building and began jumping and playing nosily. One monkey among them was very naughty. He came out of the building and went to the place where the carpenters were working.

A carpenter was sawing a huge log to cut it into two vertical halves. Just then the bell rang for the lunch break. The carpenter pushed a wedge into the split portion of the half-sawed log and went to take lunch along with other workers.

When the naughty monkey saw that there was nobody around, he came near the log and began playing with the tools lying there. Then he jumped on the half-sawed log and sat on top of it. He spread his legs on both sides of the log and his tail began dangling through the gap of the split portion.

Now the monkey began prying the wedge out of the log with his hands. Suddenly the wedge came out with a jerk. The split parts of the log snapped shut together crushing the tail of the monkey in between.

The monkey began crying with pain, but there was no one around to help him and get him out of the self-invited trouble. And due to extremely unbearable pain he died at last.

Karatak said, "This is the reason why the scholars advise not to do anything without thinking about the consequences. Such acts don't lead to happy ends."

Damanak having listened to the story intently, said, "Brother! I agree with you; but I am of the view that it is the duty of a servant to look after the job assigned by his master; and the scholars have also said that those who, due to their selfish attitude, don't think of others, can never remain happy."

Karatak said, "Well, I shall be able to prove my point by telling you the story of a donkey who was killed by his master because he began braying unnecessarily."

"How did that happen?" asked Damanak. Karatak said, "Listen to the story..."

❏ ❏

# UNNECESSARY CONCERN

There lived a washerman named Karpoorpatak in Varanasi. He had a donkey which carried loads of clothes for him, and a dog which guarded his house at night.

One night the washerman and his wife were sleeping comfortably when a thief burgled their house. The dog and the donkey both were fastened by a chain to a stake in the courtyard.

As soon as the donkey noticed the thief breaking into the house, he said, "Look, friend! A thief is burgling the house of our master."

"So what!" said the dog indifferently.

"Fool! Start barking loudly and wake up our master so that he could save his belongings from being stolen," said the donkey angrily, "now do you think it is my duty to explain to you your responsibilities? Why has the master kept you as his pet? Why do you think does the master feed you bread and milk everyday?"

"Brother, donkey! Please don't concern yourself about my responsibilities," said the dog, "it is not proper to interfere unnecessarily and bully someone. Are you not aware how I guard the house of my master day and night and how ungrateful my master is. He has become so careless about me now that he does not even give me food in time. I have decided that I shall not perform my duties until my master has stood some loss. And that is just because he doesn't care for me. He considers me a mere burden because he hasn't borne any loss for a long time. Someone has correctly said that a master doesn't give his servant's due unless he himself lands into some kind of problem."

The dog's argument irritated the donkey. He said, "O ungrateful one! Listen! A servant, who puts up his demand before his master in the time of need, is never considered loyal. You are contemplating your own profits and losses when our master is going to land into trouble." Then the donkey said again with bloodshot eyes, "All right! You may shirk your duties and responsibilities, but I am not one who would remain a silent spectator at such hour of crisis. I am going to awaken my master," and saying this the donkey began braying loudly.

The harsh sound produced by the donkey disturbed the sleep of the washerman. He became very angry. He came out with a staff in his hand and began beating the donkey mercilessly. He beat the donkey so much that his staff broke and the donkey also died.

Having narrated the story Karatak said, "Brother! This is the reason why I say that one must not act in haste and without thinking. It's not advisable to interfere with others. Our duty lies in serving our king. We search for a prey for our king. Our king hunts the prey and assuages his hunger first; and what we get is only in the form of leftovers. That's all. Here lies our limit."

"Anyway," said Damanak, "Let us go and attend our king; let's see what bothers him," saying this Damanak went to the den of the lion and prostrated himself before him. Seeing Damanak the lion said very affectionately, "Why Damanak! Where have you been all these day?"

"My Lord! You are king of this forest. We are very ordinary creatures. You hardly need us. You seldom remember us, but we always remember you."

"No, no, Damanak! You are son of our minister. How can I forget you? I have engaged you as my attendant for the only reason that you are son of my minister."

"You have been our benefactor for generations together. I cannot thank you enough for all that you have done for us. We always look for an opportunity to find favour in your eyes."

"Yes, I agree with what you say," said the lion. The lion was indeed impressed. He said, "Minister! You are really very scholarly. What you say gives me a ray of hope. A minister like you should always remain with me."

"What you say is correct, my lord. A king and his minister should never part with each other. But I would like to ask you a question if it doesn't bother you."

"Yes, yes, do ask," said the lion.

"Lord! You had gone out to drink water from the river, but you returned without drinking water. What was the reason?"

"Yes, your observation is correct. But unfortunately I couldn't find someone trustworthy with whom I could share the secret."

"You don't consider me also suitable for this?"

"No, no, it's not that."

"Then, in that case, you can share the secret with me."

"Yes, yes, I trust you. Listen—in fact, I am afraid, some very dangerous animal has entered this forest. I have heard the thunderous roar of that animal on the bank of the river. Perhaps he is destined to rule this forest in future. Because he is capable of shaking the whole of the forest with his thunderous roar."

"What are you saying, my lord?"

"I am telling you the truth. It's not difficult to asses the might of the animal with whose thunderous roar the whole of the forest begins to shake. Personally I am of the view that we must abandon the forest now."

"My Lord! I too heard the thunderous roar, but leaving one's homeland is not as simple as you think. Elders have said that brother, wife, servant, community, wisdom and self-confidence are put to test only when there is a challenge."

"Damanak! I have explained to you my problem. I don't know what is going to happen now."

"My Lord! You would not have become nervous, had you not been worried. But you need not worry so long as we are with you. We two brothers shall manage the situation. Please don't be ill at ease; leave it to us to unravel the mystery."

"Yes, yes, do everything you brothers can. From my side you two are absolutely free."

"Thank you, my lord! With your blessings we shall return only after we have found out your enemy."

Damanak returned and explained everything in detail to Karatak. "Brother! Do you think this will make our king overcome his fear now?" asked Karatak.

"Perhaps!"

"But you have promised the king that we shall return only after we have traced his enemy."

"Brother! This is politics. Politics says that it's no sin even if one has to tell lies to make the king happy. It is necessary to be brave and wise if one wants to oblige someone. You may not be aware, but I know the reason why our king is so frightened."

"And what's that reason?"

"In fact there is a bullock who lives along the bank of the river. Our king has only heard him bellowing; he has not yet seen him. And that is the reason why he is so scared."

"If it was as simple as that, you should have made the king aware of it. What is the use of keeping him worried?"

Damanak said, "Brother! No one is going to honour us if we solve a problem without any difficulty. How will the king know that we are wise ministers? Our politics says that a king should not be allowed to become free from fear. And if you commit this kind of mistake you too will suffer like the cat did."

"What's the story?"

"Listen, I shall tell you the story."

❏ ❏

# 4

# A CAT'S FALLACY

Durdant, a lion, lived on a mountain in the north named Aburd Shikhar. He was brave and strong and lived in a den, in which there lived a mouse also.

Whenever the lion slept in the den, the mouse would come out of the hole and gnaw at his mane. This was very irritating for him to see every morning his mane gnawed at by the mouse. And the irony was that the lion, despite being so brave and strong, was unable to punish the mouse.

One day, getting a chance, the lion pounced on the mouse angrily, but the mouse was swift enough to rush into the hole before the lion could take him in his grip. This irritated the lion all the more. He began thinking—'if the enemy is too small in size, it is impossible to overpower him for someone who is big and strong. Only someone of his size can teach him a lesson or bring an end to his life."

Thinking thus he was passing through the forest when he happened to see a cat in the way. Cats and lions are considered of the same species. And so it didn't take them time to come close to each other. The lion made friends with the cat and took him to his den.

The lion always extended the best possible hospitality to the cat. He used to give him fresh and tasty meat to eat. He used to talk to him respectfully and sweetly. One day the mouse happened to see the cat in the den, and was quick to understand that the lion had made friends with the cat only in order to get rid of him. In a way it was true also. And for fear of the cat the mouse stopped coming out of the hole.

The lion had gotten rid of the mouse, but he was always afraid that the mouse might come out of the hole and, getting a chance, might gnaw at his mane again.

On the other side, the poor mouse had totally stopped coming out of the hole. Who does'nt love one's life!

Not seeing the mouse for days together the lion thought—"Either the mouse has abandoned this cave and gone away, or he may have died, or, it's quite likely, the cat might have devoured him."

One day the lion went out to take a stroll in the forest. The cat was sitting alone in the den. The mouse, who was almost on the verge of death due to starvation, came out of the hole and began searching for food. He had taken every care to keep himself out of sight of the cat, but the always alert cat saw him without letting the mouse notice it. And next moment the cat pounced on the mouse, killed it and ate it.

The lion returned in the evening and offered fresh and tasty meat to the cat with great affection. After some time the lion went to sleep. It was a pleasant surprise for the lion that he did not notice any movement of the mouse that night.

Next day the lion asked the cat casually, "Friend! The mouse is not to be seen around. Has he died or he is hiding out of fear?"

"O king of the forest! You need not worry any more. I have killed your enemy. Hence forth he will not be seen here. Now we shall live in this den comfortably."

"Yes, yes! Why not? My friend! It is because of you that I have gotten rid of such irritating problem. I could never enjoy a good sleep throughout the night so long as the mouse was alive."

Of course the lion expressed his gratitude to the cat, but he didn't mean it. He had his own machinations. The lion was thinking—'How do I need this cat now! It was only for the wicked mouse that I had brought him to my den. Now that he has killed and devoured the mouse, he is of no use to me.'

The selfish lion stopped bringing food for the cat from the next day. All that he gave him to eat was nothing more than leftovers, and that too, very unwillingly. Poor cat had no choice but to accept whatever given. From that day onwards he never got enough food to eat his fill. He began starving. It had become clear to him that the lion offered him fresh and tasty meat only so long as he needed his help. Once he killed his enemy his services were not required any more. How long could the cat survive under those circumstances? He began losing weight, and a day came when he succumbed to death.

Having narrated this story Damanak said to Karatak—"Brother! Everyone in this world is full of selfishness. People are interested in serving their ends only."

Talking thus, they reached the bank of the river. They saw there Sanjeevak sitting on green grass and ruminating. They said, "O bullock! Are you not aware that we have been entrusted with the responsibility of safety of this zone."

"Are you two guarding this zone?"

"Yes!" said Damanak.

"But I have done no harm to anyone."

"How can you say that you have done no harm to anyone? The biggest mistake that you have committed is that you have not gone to the lion to offer your salutations to him. The law in this forest is that anyone, who enters this forest as an outsider, has to offer his salutations to the king of this forest. Did you observe this rule?"

"I am sorry, I did not."

"Isn't this kind of failure an arrogance on your part? If you want safety of your life you must accompany us to the king and offer your salutations. And then it will be for him to decide the future course of action. We are no more than servants."

Hearing the name of the lion the bullock began trembling with fear.

"What are you thinking? You want to live in this forest or not?"

"Look, brothers! I am only a bullock. You also know that I don't belong to this forest. If you take me to your king, what is the guarantee that I shall return alive? Brothers! I am innocent! No one apprised me of the rules and regulations of this forest."

"O bullock! Don't fear! Our king is very kind-hearted. He takes full care of his subjects. He is not one who would think bad of others. He is always worried about the welfare of everyone. Have no fear! Let's go to our king. We are sure he will extend his forgiveness to you."

"Do you two promise to take care of safety of my life," asked Sanjeevak suspiciously.

"Don't worry! We shall take full care of you," said Karatak, "our king always values our requests and suggestions. We shall tell him that this bullock is very gentle and innocent."

Assured thus by the jackals the bullock prepared himself to go with them. He had neither sinned nor had he cheated anyone throughout his life. He had a very clean heart. He considered everyone as simple as he himself was. And so he proceeded with them without a tinge of doubt in his mind.

Pingalak, the lion, saw the jackals coming with the bullock. He immediately went in and sat on his throne, and began waiting for them.

Damanak and Karatak were the first to enter the den and offer their salutations to their king. Sanjeevak followed them and he too bowed with reverence.

Damanak whispered in the ear of his king, "My Lord! Please do not be afraid of him. Talk to him in the manner a king does. Elders say that fearing a sound without knowing its source is not wise. It is for this kind of alertness that a procuress was honoured by a king."

"How did that happen?"

"Listen! I shall tell you a story."

❏ ❏

# 5

# THE MYSTERY OF THE BELL

On mountain Shree was situated a town named Brahmapur.

The townspeople of Brahmapur believed that there lived a demon, Ghantakarna, on the mountain top, because they often heard the sound of ringing of bell coming from the top.

The townspeople had also seen a structure of a skeleton there which caused them to form an idea that the demon used to kill people and devour them. Whereas the fact was that a thief stole a golden bell from the temple of Lord Shiva which was outside the village and out of fear of being caught the thief ran toward the mountain where he was killed and eaten up by a lion.

After some time a group of monkeys happened to arrive at the place where the thief was lying dead. They picked up the golden bell and began ringing it again and again.

Hearing the ringing of bell every now and then and seeing a skeleton the townspeople were made to believe that the mountain top was the residence of the demon, Ghantakarana.

And it was for fear of the demon that the townspeople began making preparations to abandon the town.

The king seeing his subjects fleeing thus, became very sad. He sent many of his soldiers to unravel the mystery of the ringing of the bell. But none of the soldiers dared go to the mountain top; instead they returned and informed the king that there indeed was a demon who was not visible and was in a habit of calling people by ringing his bell and eating them. The king became very sad to hear this. He arranged to make an announcement that one who would succeed in locating the demon and informing the king his whereabouts will be rewarded suitably.

In the same town there lived also a procuress who too used to hear the sound of ringing of bell from time to time. She was very curious as to who it was who rang bell at such odd hours. She thought—'Devotees ring bells during the time of worship only. There must be some mystery behind all this. These townspeople are running away from the town unnecessarily. They must be mad. But I shall definitely unravel the mystery of the bell,' and thinking thus she began climbing the mountain.

There she saw a group of monkeys at a distance. One of the monkeys in the group took the bell and began ringing it loudly. The procuress understood the mystery of the bell. "These naughty monkeys are ringing this bell and frightening the townspeople," thought she to herself.

The procuress returned from there. She was very happy. She had found out who Ghantakarna was who had terrorized everyone.

She went straight to the king and said, "My Lord! I can arrange to have the demon, Ghantakarna, arrested."

"Do you really think you can do it?"

"Yes, my lord! You may trust me, and if you have any doubts you may send a team of soldiers with me so that they may also see what kind of demon Ghantakarna is and how I take complete control of him.

The king nodded in agreement and sent a team of his chosen soldiers with the procuress.

The procuress was leading the team of soldiers. She was aware that monkeys love eating bananas. And so, she bought dozens and dozens of bananas in the way. Having made all preparations she began climbing the mountain fearlessly. Reaching the mountain top she threw the bananas before the group of monkeys. Seeing bananas in abundance, the monkeys threw away the bell and began eating the bananas thrown by her.

The procuress picked up the bell and returned with it to the king along with the team of soldiers, and placing it before him she said, "My lord! This is the demon, Ghantakarna. This was in the possession of a group of monkeys who had driven our townspeople mad, and out of fear of whom they were running away from the town."

The king was mighty pleased to see her courage and rewarded her handsomely. It was because of the wits and wisdom of the procuress that the townspeople were greatly relieved.

"And precisely for this reason I say, O king!" said Damanak, "try always to know the truth behind everything. Doubts and false notions don't help in any manner. It's your false notion that is making you fear this bullock. Make friends with him. This friendship will make you all the more strong."

On the advice of the jackal, the lion gave the bullock a high status and made him sit by the side of his throne.

Now the lion was no more afraid of the bullock, and the bullock was happy that he had made friends with someone of whom everyone was afraid.

Both these friends were enjoying their time together, when the lion's younger brother happened to pay a visit to their place. The lion went out hunting for his younger brother and took Sanjeevak also along. While still in the way Sanjeevak asked the lion, "Friend! Where is the remaining flesh that you had kept in your den after eating yesterday?"

"Yes, friend! Now I remember. I had killed a wild boar yesterday. I had saved a large chunk of flesh for next day, but now I find that there is nothing left. It seems the two jackals have devoured it."

"But how can they act in this manner without your permission?"

"How to tell you, my friend! They take too much liberty with me, and it is probably because I don't say anything to them."

"But this is not proper. After all you are a king; and if someone even touches something that belongs to you, should not be spared. It's a crime."

"That means what they have done is highly improper."

"I am talking of ethics only, my friend! It's very important for any king to keep his eyes open and see if his friend is betraying him."

"Your teachings are very didactic, friend! But what to do? They don't listen to me. They always act according to their will," said the lion in a sad tone.

The lion was considering himself lucky to have Sanjeevak as his friend. From that day onwards the lion appointed Sanjeevak the caretaker of the flesh he brought to his den.

This made things change. All the manoeuvres of the jackal brothers came to a still. One day Damanaka said to Karatak, "Brother! What to do now? All our life we have been sitting and eating without doing anything. Now we are like that prince who touched the picture of Swarnarekha and lost all his happiness."

"How?"

"Listen! I shall tell you the story," said Damanak.

❑ ❑

# 6

# AS YOU SOW, SO YOU WILL REAP

There was a time when Kanchanpur was ruled by King Veervikram Singh. Once a barber committed some crime for which he was arrested and was to be brought before the king. Just then a saint happened to come there. He enquired about the crime committed by the barber, and on being told he could immediately make out that the barber was going to be subjected to nothing less than capital punishment.

He requested the soldiers of the king to free the barber.

"No, Maharaj! How is it possible to free a criminal? He must be punished for the crime committed by him."

"No, you must free him," said the saint angrily.

"But this has not happened till date that a criminal may have been left unpunished."

"This has happened. You may not be aware of it. Let me tell you..."

"You must have heard the name of Sinhal island. Jibhootketu was the king of that island, and I am his son Kandarvaketu."

"One day I was sitting in my garden. Just then a trader happened to come there having disembarked from a ship. He came near me and said—"Look! On the fourteenth day of the lunar month a young girl appears from the sea laden with various kinds of jewellery, sitting on a throne studded with gems. She is seen playing Veena; and when you see her, you will be compelled to liken her to goddess Lakshmi herself."

I listened to him carefully and then accompanied him in the ship to the place which he had described. Oh, my God! She was beautiful beyond description. I immediately fell in love with her. I was so enamoured of her charm that without thinking another moment I dived into the sea.

Next moment, I was in a palace in which I saw the beautiful girl sitting adorned with beautiful clothing and jewellery. Many celestial damsels were attending upon her. As soon as she saw me she signalled to her maids to leave. And then she began talking to me.

She told me that her name was Ratan Manjari and she was a princess. She said that she had taken a vow that she would marry only that person who came to the palace and saw her. I fulfilled her condition and was married to her.

Ratan Manjari also said to me, "O darling! Everything that belongs to me is also yours, I am yours, this country is yours; but be very careful! Never ever touch the celestial damsel Swarnarekha."

This was such a strange instruction that I became very curious to know the mystery of Swarnarekha. I wanted to know why my wife had instructed me not to touch her.

A day came when I did touch her. And the moment I touched her I was catapulted back to my kingdom. I began shedding tears thinking how severely someone is punished for his foolish mistakes.

This was such an experience that I lost all my interests in the worldly life. I abandoned everything and it is since then that I have been wandering about in the form of a Sanyasin.

One day I stayed in the house of a cowherd. It so happened that when the cowherd returned after having grazed his cattle, he saw a procuress talking to his wife. That procuress had brought some message of the lover of the cowherd's wife. This made the cowherd so angry that he beat her badly and tied her to a pole in the house.

As soon as it began getting dark, the lover of the cowherd's wife sent the procuress again to her with his message. She said, "Your lover is in a very pitiable condition. He is shedding tears for you."

"Sister! Just see how helpless I am right now. My husband has tied me. He comes every few minutes to check and see that I am present here."

The procuress laughed and said, "Is that all! That's not a big problem. My dear sister! You must not fear if you are in love with someone. I too shall make a little sacrifice. I shall fulfill the duties of a messenger."

"How will you help me, sister?"

"I shall replace you by myself and allow you to go and meet your lover. I shall return when you come back."

"Not a bad idea!" said the cowherds wife and became very happy at this proposal.

The procuress, who was in fact a barber's wife, undid the knots of the wife of the cowherd and got herself tied in her place.

The cowherd suddenly woke up around midnight. He was still boiling with anger. He went to the place where he had tied his wife and said, "You slut, you cheat, you immoral woman! Come, I shall take you to your father right now. Your case will be decided there only. You have cheated me; you have broken my heart; you are a sinner!"

The barber's wife had hidden her face completely by the end of her Sari. She knew that speaking a single word would disclose her identity. She decided to keep mum.

This added to the anger of the cowherd. He rushed to his kitchen, brought a knife from there and slashed her nose.

The barber's wife screamed with pain. Her nose began bleeding vehemently.

When the cowherd's wife returned after meeting her lover, she saw the slashed nose of the barber's wife and her pasty face smeared with blood. She shrieked with terror and asked in a trembling voice, "What is this! O God! Who has done this to you?"

"Have patience, sister! Don't say a word. If it had not been I, it would have been you. One of us had to face this problem. One has to bear the consequences of the sins committed by him/her.

The cowherd's wife freed the barber's wife, and the barber's wife returned home after tying the cowherd's wife again to the same pole.

The barber while leaving for his shop in the morning asked his wife to give him his tools.

The barber's wife was already very much in pain. She could manage to get only a razor in a hurry; and instead of giving it to him in his hand, she threw it toward him from a distance. In fact she had done this on purpose. The barber became furious to see only one razor in place of the set of tools. He threw the razor toward his wife and said, "O foolish woman! Do you think I can manage my job with this razor only?"

The barber's wife was successful in accomplishing her aim. This is what she had wanted. She knew that giving one razor only would infuriate her husband.

She began screaming—"O God! Look at this cruel man! He has mutilated me. He has cut my nose.

The neighbours and the soldiers of the king, all collected there to hear her screaming at the top of her voice. They arrested the barber. On the other side, the cowherd, when he woke up in the morning, began feeling sorry for having mutilated his wife. He went to his wife and began untying the knots of the rope with which he had tied her; but suddenly his hands stopped.

"Darling! Why did your hands stop suddenly? Please untie the knot. See, my body is aching."

The cowherd began trembling with fear. He said, "I had slashed your nose last night, but..."

"Yes, you did, but I am a chaste woman. I have such divine power that no man can harm me. You can see for yourself that I have proven my chastity now. The sun, moon, air, fire, sky, earth, water, heart, god of death, day, night, morning and evening, all are aware of the good and bad deeds of human beings. I am chaste, but you blamed me without basis and mutilated me. Since God is aware of my chasteness, my nose has remained unharmed. I possess the divine power of a chaste woman, and, if I want, I can burn you to ashes with my power, but I won't do so because you are my husband."

"Please forgive me! I made a mistake," said the cowherd.

This was the story of the sinful woman who, having cheated her husband, succeeded in proving herself a chaste woman. Now I shall tell you the story of a saint who had just returned from the Himalayas after leading an austere life for twelve years. Only God knows his fate. But it is saddening to see people of such status committing mistakes. Now listen—

While the saint was returning after leading an austere life, it began getting dark. He went and slept in the house of a prostitute. While the saint was deep asleep the prostitute noticed a piece of diamond as a pendant attached to the string of beads around his neck. The greed for diamond got the better of her. She tried to steal the diamond from his necklace, but the saint woke up. He caught her red-handed.

"Look, saint! You know it only too well that I am a prostitute, and prostitutes love money only. I like this diamond! Either you give it to me without creating any fuss or I am going to tell everyone that you had come to burgle my house," said the prostitute.

The saint was shocked to hear this. He immediately gave away the piece of diamond to the prostitute and out of fear for her he came running straight to me. On the other side the innocent barber was awarded death sentence for having committed the crime of slashing the nose of his wife. The barber told everything about his wife to the king with tears in his eyes. The king was wise. He immediately deployed his spies to find out everything in detail about the barber's wife. On being enquired, the barber's wife told them that it was the wife of the cowherd who was to be blamed; she was in a habit of cheating her husband. Having come to know the truth the king ordered that the barber's wife, cowherd's wife and her lover be imprisoned and the innocent barber be freed.

"And so, brother...!" said Damanak, "First get to know the truth and then decide your course of action. It is mainly our fault that we arranged friendship between the bullock and the lion."

"But why do you forget that if we can make them friends we may as well make them enemies of each other."

"You think you can do it?"

"Yes, the scholars say that witty people can very cleverly turn truth into falsehood; like a milkmaid had done in trying to save her lover."

"What's the story of the milkmaid?"

"Listen! I am telling you," and Damanak began telling the story of the milkmaid to Karatak.

❏ ❏

# 7

# CROOKEDNESS

A very long time ago there lived a milkman named Bansi in Dwarvati town. His wife was a real adulteress.

Of her two lovers, one was a General of army and the other was the General's son.

So the milkmaid was making happy her husband, the General and his son, all at the same time.

Once it so happened that when she was having a good time with the son of the General, the General also happened to arrive there.

As soon as the milkmaid heard the footsteps of the General, she quickly hid the boy in a corner and then opened the door.

She allowed the General to come in and bolted the door from inside. She began having a good time with the General also, but coincidentally her husband too happened to come at the same time.

Generally, under such circumstances, the brains of women of infidelity start working very fast. She said to the General, "Leave this place at once, striking the ground with your staff, as if you had come here searching for someone. No one will doubt your presence here. Rest I shall manage."

The General followed her advice. He came out of her room striking the floor with his staff.

The milkman came in and asked his wife, "Why had the General come here?"

"In fact the General had become very angry with his son for some unknown reasons. His son, out of fear for his father, came to my room and hid himself here. He had come here in search of his son. Now since he has gone away, I am going to tell his son to return home."

Saying this the milkmaid signalled to the boy to come out. She said, "Go back home now. It's not good to quarrel among yourselves. You are no more a small child that you are bothering your parents thus."

The boy understood how tactfully the milkmaid had handled the case. He immediately went out of the room. The milkmaid managed the case so skilfully that the milkman could not have the slightest doubt about her integrity. She began talking to her husband sweetly and her husband ignored even what he had seen with his own eyes.

This is the reason why I say that we shall have to be very careful in managing this issue.

"Brother! Is it possible for us to create a rift between the lion and the bullock."

"We shall at least have to try. Success or failure is something that comes later. One can do anything in the world if he tries. Something that cannot be done with might, can be done with wits. It was by using their wits that the male and female crows managed to get the snake killed and save their chicks."

"How did that happen?"

"Listen!" and Damanak began telling the story.

# 8

# SOLUTION TO A PROBLEM

In the dense forests of Bijapur there was a Peepal tree on the bank of a river. A crow and his wife lived on a branch of it. They loved each other very much. Their love was such that they would not separate from each other even for a single moment.

They would set out in search of food early in the morning and return together in the evening. In a way they were very happy in each other's company. Their only bother was that they had no issue.

One day when the female crow conveyed the good news to her husband that she was in the family way, the male crow began dancing happily. That day they wandered about aimlessly enjoying their time. Then the crow went and brought some good food for his wife.

They became parents after a few days. It was real good time for them. Both would go out everyday and bring tasty food for their chicks, and feed them with great affection.

But on an unfortunate day when they returned with food for their chicks in the evening, they were shocked to see them missing.

Both husband and wife kept weeping throughout the night. Ultimately they lost all their hopes and compromised with their fate.

The crow could very well understand that it was some enemy of his who was behind the cruel act. He knew that his enemy was the black snake who lived in a hole in the roots of the tree. But he also knew that it was not possible for him to fight with the snake.

The female crow conceived once again after some time. She lay her eggs when the time came. This time she was very watchful so that nothing untoward happened. The male crow used to go alone in search of food.

One day the female crow said to her husband, "Look, darling! Now the time has come when our chicks may emerge any day by breaking the shell. But the snake will eat them up again. I think it would be better if we made some arrangements beforehand."

"Darling! Don't you worry. I have been sparing this snake till now for one simple reason that he is our neighbour; but now since he has become our enemy, I don't consider it right to spare him any more."

"But how would you manage to counter this poisonous snake?"

"Darling!" said the male crow, "I know our enemy is much stronger than us, but it's not only physical might that solves every problem. Your physical strength has no meaning if you are not witty. This snake possesses poison as his weapon, and it is because of his poison that he considers himself very strong."

"Still he is stronger than us."

"Darling! One who possesses wits possesses might also. Have you not heard the story of the lion who was killed by a rabbit?"

"How is it possible for a rabbit to kill a lion?"

"Listen to the story if you don't believe in what I say," said the crow and began narrating the story.

❏ ❏

# 9

# USING ONE'S WITS

There lived a lion named Durdant on Mandar mountain. Because he was very strong he would kill small and big animals and eat them. He was so cruel that whichever side he went, bodies of a number of dead animals could be seen strewn all around. He would eat one or two animals and leave the rest to be devoured by jackals and foxes.

Troubled by the atrocities committed by the lion, the sad-stricken animals of the forest called for a meeting and elected the peacock to convene the meeting. All the animals of the forest assembled to find a solution to the problem.

All the animals assembled there, decided in unison to approach the lion and request him not to kill innocent animals unnecessarily. They decided to make an offer to the lion that they would send one animal a day to his den for his meals.

The proposal was gladly accepted by the lion. From that day it became a regular practice in the forest that one animal, on his turn, would go to the den of the lion and the lion would make a meal of him sitting comfortably in his den. Now every animal in the forest knew the day when he would become the meal of the lion and breathe his last.

One day it was the turn of a rabbit to become a meal of the lion. Coincidentally he had just become a father of two young ones. He didn't want to go, but was helpless.

He began thinking of some ruse to get himself out of the trouble. Suddenly he hit upon a bright idea; and the idea was such that he was hundred percent sure of its success. He set out fearlessly toward the den of the lion. He had full confidence in his plan. There was an old well in the way. He halted there for some time, took rest and then proceeded further. It was in fact on purpose that he was delaying.

Ultimately he reached the den of the lion much after his lunch time. The lion became terribly angry to see him coming so late.

He roared angrily, "Why did you come so late? Where were you? I am dying of hunger. Even if I eat you I shall remain hungry because you are too small in size.

"Your Majesty!" said the rabbit, "I am not to be blamed for the delay. If I am late it is because of the other lion who began chasing me while I was on the way to your den. He wanted to eat me and was saying that he too was the king of the forest."

The lion roared angrily and said, "Impossible! There cannot exist two kings in a forest. I shall kill him. Tell me where he lives."

"Your Majesty! There is a well nearby. The other lion is hiding in it."

"All right!" said the lion, "Guide me to the well."

The rabbit took the lion to a deep well which was full of water.

"Your Majesty!" said the rabbit, "You may see for yourself that the other lion is hiding inside this well."

The lion climbed up the puteal of the well and peeped in. He saw his own reflection in the water and, thinking that it was the other lion who had challenged his authority, jumped into the well.

Thus, the rabbit succeeded in his plan and the lion drowned.

Someone has correctly said—"Wit is more powerful than mere strength."

Hearing the story from the crow his wife said, "Look, darling! I have listened to your story patiently. Now it's time when we should worry about the safety of our chicks. The black snake is sitting all prepared to devour our chicks."

"Yes, yes, that's what I am upto. Look, darling! A prince comes to bathe everyday in the nearby pond. Before getting into the pond he takes out all his jewellery and puts them on the edge of the pond. There is one very expensive string of beads of pearls which forms part of his jewellery. I have planned to fly away with it."

"What will happen then?"

"That you will see for yourself," said the crow.

Next day the crow flew to the pond early in the morning. The prince came there to bathe and took out his clothes and jewellery, and put them on one side.

Just then the crow took the necklace in its beak and flew away with it toward his home. The soldiers saw the crow flying away with the necklace and began chasing him.

The crow dropped the necklace near the hole of the snake. The snake became very happy to see the necklace of pearls. He picked it up and entered the hole.

The soldiers saw the snake going into the hole with the necklace. They, after digging up the hole, saw the snake sitting coiled on it. They immediately killed the snake and went away with the necklace.

The crow, thus, became very happy on the death of his enemy.

After hearing this story Damanaka said to Karataka, "Brother! If that be so, please find some way. I wish that we should be in the good books of our master again."

"All right, brother! I shall give it one more try."

There could be no creature on earth as hostile and cunning as a jackal. And these two brothers were managing their meals for a long time without having to do anything. Now it was impossible for them to labour for their meals. They were almost on the point of starvation. They contemplated the issue for a long time and then decided to go to Pingalak.

When they offered their salutations to their old master, Pingalak, the king of the forest, he said, "Hello brothers, Damanak and Karatak! How are you two? Tell me the purpose of your visit."

"Lord! We are fine. In fact we saw in the dream last night that you are going to get into some kind of trouble. We are your servants, Lord. The treatises command that a servant should not hesitate to sacrifice his life for his master, if required."

"What is it that you want to say?" asked Pingalak in a surprised tone.

"Lord! You are our king. We are fully aware that you are not happy with us. But what you are not aware of is that Sanjeevak, who is your best friend, does not belong to the forests. He is not fit to become our friends, because we are carnivorous and he is herbivorous. Now just think, how is it possible to become our friend. In fact he has developed friendship with you so that he may kill you at some opportune time and himself become the king of this forest."

"What is it that you are saying?"

"We are saying only what Sanjeevak said to us yesterday. He has separated us from you only to clear his way." Karataka, the other jackal said, "Lord! One must get rid of poisonous food, loose tooth and a wicked minister. I have come here only to alert you, and that too for one simple reason that not only I, but my ancestors too are indebted to you."

"All right! Even if I go by what you say, I shall have to rethink, because Sanjeevaka is a friend of mine."

"Lord! This is where you are making a mistake. Why don't you try to understand that once you are dominated you are dominated for ever."

"But a creature who does not belong to our species has extended his affection like a brother to me. Why would he cheat me?"

"Lord! It is our duty to put you on your alert, because you have extended favour to us for years together."

"You mean to say that I should ask him to leave this place," asked the lion.

"Lord! If you ask him to leave this place all of a sudden, I am afraid the secret might be unveiled even before getting to the real truth."

The lion was impressed indeed. He said to the jackals, "I get your point. Do one thing—keep an eye on Sanjeevak and keep me informed of his activities and plans."

"Lord! It's not advisable to draw any conclusion before gathering complete information about him including that of his physical might. And only then we should get into action. Have you not heard about the peewit, who despite being a very ordinary bird made hell the life of a sea?"

"What's that story?" asked the lion.

"Listen to the story of the peewit," saying this Damanak began narrating the story.

❏ ❏

# 10

# WHEN THE SEA WAS VANQUISHED

There lived a pair of peewits on a seashore. Both together had built a home for themselves in the sand. They were living happily together. After some time the female peewit became pregnant. The male and female peewits were so excited about it that they began making future plans for their would-be chick.

One day the female peewit said to her husband, "Darling! Earlier we were only two and had no reason to fear. But now since I am expecting, we shall have to shift to some safe place. This will keep our chicks out of danger."

"Darling!" said the male peewit, "Do you think the sea will subject us to torments because we are weak?"

"You are being strange," said the female peewit, "I don't think there is anything wrong in what I say. Just think coolly and tell me if there is any similarity between us and him."

"Darling! Remember one thing. One who is capable of differentiating a suitable one from on unsuitable one and is also capable of vanquishing his enemy, won't be saddened by the most difficult circumstances. Scholars say that there are four ways of inviting death :

1. Involving oneself in bad and wrong deeds.
2. Standing in opposition of the dear ones.
3. Fighting with an enemy who is more powerful than him.
4. Trusting a woman.

Despite all the genuine advises, the female peewit was adamant that they should change their place before she delivers her chicks.

But her husband was no less adamant, and maintained that no change of place would take place. His argument was that it was not possible to build a home everyday. Ultimately the female peewit had to give in.

The sea was listening intently to their arguments. He wanted to see the ultimate result.

Finally, the female peewit had to surrender and lay her eggs on the seashore. One day the husband and wife went a little too far in search of food. Taking advantage of the opportunity the sea waves washed away their eggs. As soon as the pair of peewits returned, they realized that their eggs had been washed away by the sea. The female peewit began wailing loudly.

Seeing her wailing her husband said, "Darling! Please do not worry. I shall retrieve your eggs for sure."

Having assured his wife thus, he went and met his friends and narrated the whole sequence of happenings. He was extremely sad. Seeing him sad-stricken his friends too were saddened. Meanwhile, a parrot, one of his friends, said, "Brother! It's no use lamenting the mishappening. We shall have to deal with this case a little tactfully."

"Brother parrot! I am totally uneducated. I know nothing about tactfulness. I am depending solely on you all. It is for you to decide our course of action. I shall co-operate in every respect."

"Look, brother! Everyone in the world knows that the sea is mighty powerful and unchallengeable. We are too weak before him. Yes, in case we have to avenge ourselves, we shall have to approach Garuda Ji. He is king of birds and the mode of conveyance of Lord Vishnu. He will definitely provide succour to us."

Accepting the advice of the parrot all the birds approached Garuda Ji along with the peewit and offered their salutations to him.

"Brothers! Tell me the purpose of your visit."

The peewit stepped forward and said, "Lord! I am a peewit living on the seashore along with my wife. The sea has done great injustice to us. While we were away in search of food, the sea waves washed away our eggs."

Garuda Ji listened to the peewit intently and then said, "You need not worry. I shall do whatever I can to provide succour to you."

Assured thus, the birds left, and Garuda Ji approached Lord Vishnu in order to submit their case before him. Lord Vishnu said, "There must be some special purpose behind your sudden visit."

"Lord! The sea is being greatly unjust to bird species."

"What kind of injustice? Tell me, dear!"

"The sea waves washed away the eggs of the peewits living on the seashore. All the birds are terribly shocked to see the torments of the sea. Lord! Subjecting birds to such torments is highly objectionable."

"All right, Garuda! I shall discuss the matter with the sea right now and ask him as to what prompted him to act in such a cruel manner," saying this Lord Vishnu set out to meet the sea along with Garuda.

As soon as the sea noticed Lord Vishnu coming toward him, he offered his salutations and said humbly, "O Lord! What made you take the trouble of coming to me? If at all I was required, you could have ordered me to come and see you."

"O god of seas! I have been informed that you have stolen away the eggs of a pair of peewits. What wrong had they done to you after all?"

The sea began trembling with fear. He said to Lord Vishnu, "Lord! I am sorry and admit that I have committed a mistake. I am ready to obey supreme command, whatsoever it may be."

"I order you to return their eggs immediately."

"As you wish, O Lord!" saying this the sea returned the eggs of the peewits."

The husband and wife were too pleased to get their eggs back. They made friends with the sea.

After narrating the story the jackal said, "Lord! This is world. There are great cheats all around. Like the peewit, this bullock also considers you too weak in the absence of your ministers."

The lion was lost in thoughts to hear what the jackal said. He was compelled to think that the jackal bore at least some truth in his version. He thought that the jackal had a point in saying that a lion and a bullock cannot become natural friends, because they belonged to entirely different species.

Now both the jackals were happy that they had succeeded in creating a rift between Pingalak and Sanjeevak.

Sanjeevak noticed some change in the lion when they met next. The lion was staring at him.

"Hello friend! You seem to be lost in thoughts. Are you all right?"

"Friend! You know it very well that I am king of this forest. The responsibility of all my subjects lies on me. But then it will become impossible for me to maintain my normal health when I realize that I am being cheated by someone who is one of my subjects."

"You are talking strange, my friend, today," said the bullock in a surprised tone.

"Brother! None except my fate is to be blamed for this. I am like a creature who is drowning and happens to hold a snake in trying to survive. If he leaves the snake, he will drown, and if he keeps holding it, he is sure to be bitten by it. The problem that I am facing is tiring me mentally; because right now I am not able to judge as to whom to trust and whom not to."

"Brother! What is it that you want to say after all? What is it that makes you feel so disappointed?" asked the bullock.

"Right now I am not in a position to tell you anything, because I am unable to think clearly. Let the time come and we shall have an open discussion," saying this the lion returned.

The two jackals came and met the bullock as soon as the lion left. They had eavesdropped on the conversation between the lion and the bullock. They were extremely happy on the success of their divide and rule policy.

"Hello, brother Sanjeevak! How are you?"

"Fine! Thank you!"

"But you don't look fine. It seems you have quarrelled with our king on some issue. Generally kings are very unpredictable. They may do anything any time, especially our king, Pingalaka."

"Why brother! What's so strange about our king?"

"Brother Sanjeevak! It would be unethical if we say something about it. Already our species has a bad name for it. But you must remember that we were the ones who had arranged friendship between you and the lion."

"Yes, yes, I remember it only too well."

"Brother Sanjeevak! Now how to tell you? It won't be proper for us to say anything."

"What is it that you are so much afraid of disclosing? You must not hesitate in opening your heart to someone who is none other than your own friend."

"Brother Sanjeevak! It is with great reservation that we are telling you that our king seems to be inclined towards evil. At least one thing you know for sure that he is a carnivorous animal. He may change his mind any moment. And this precisely is the situation that we are anticipating. The day he is hungry, and is not able to get a prey, he is sure to kill and devour you."

"How can you say that? He is after all my friend."

"Yes, he is. But this friendship was arranged by us only. We had brought you to the lion. But friend! Had we been aware of the selfishness of the lion, we would not have arranged this friendship. After all he is a carnivoures animal. No matter how much he might change himself, but his natural instincts will prevail. This lion is like the tail of a dog which can never be straightened. Now, friend! We won't like to say much about it. Kindly allow us to take leave of you. Only God knows what lies in the womb of the future," saying this the jackals left.

The poor bullock was very simple at heart. He thought, "I have never contemplated any evil designs; but the lion seems to have his own machinations. And under such circumstances it would be very cowardly for me to run away for safety of my life. Death is inevitable. Even if I try to run away, the lion, being the king of the forest, won't spare my life."

Meanwhile the jackals went and approached the lion. They said, "Lord! We had just been to Sanjeevak. You would be surprised to know that Sanjeevak has clearly mentioned that he has his plans to kill you and become the king of the forest. He went to the extent that he would challenge you for a duel tomorrow itself and decide the matter once for all. He also said that he could no more remain your slave."

"Is it that he is ready to fight with me?"

"Yes, yes! Look, Lord! Perhaps he is coming this side only. Just look at his horns; look at his bloodshot eyes. He seems to be ready to fight till death. Be alert, O Lord! or else he might kill you," said Damanaka adding fuel to fire, "We are sure he wants to replace you as king."

The jackals were getting success after success. They were fully successful in their plans. Suddenly, the lion, in a paroxysm of anger, roared loudly, and made it evident that he was hell-bent to enter into a combat with the bullock.

And for Sanjeevak it was only a confirmation of what the jackals had warned him about.

The lion was now all prepared for a combat. Though the bullock had no such intentions, seeing the lion's preparedness for a fight, he too readied himself.

But the jackals, sitting at a safe distance, were laughing in their hearts, thinking that they had ultimately succeeded in their plans.

A fierce fighting ensued between the lion and the bullock. Since both were strong, the duel continued for quite some time. But a bullock is after all a bullock. He could not match the might of the lion. The lion too had been badly injured, and was bleeding profusely; but he ultimately won. Sanjeevak breathed his last owing to vital injuries.

Though the lion had won the battle, he was extremely sad to see his friend lying dead. He began thinking—'Death of a wise servant or a friend is like the death of the king himself. A lost piece of land could be regained, but a friend lost is lost for ever,' and tears welled up in his eyes.

But on the contrary the jackals were very happy. They came laughing and dancing to the lion and said, "Lord! It's no use shedding tears now. After all he was our enemy; why should we grieve over his death. And then, above all, this bullock didn't belong to our land. He was an outsider. Forget him. Look, at least we are loyal to you. Now please come. Let's go. Brush off everything and take care of your kingdom. What, if you lost a bullock; we two, your ministers, are here."

Sad-stricken Pingalak looked at the jackals and then cast his eyes on Sanjeevak, lying dead. But what is done cannot be undone. He could never know that the cunning jackals were instrumental in getting Sanjeevak, his friend, killed; Sanjeevak—who was wise and honest, both.

Having finished the story Vishnu Sharma said, "This was Suhrid-Bhed which all of you heard."

"Guru Ji! We are extremely pleased to hear this story. It's so very kind of you."

In reply, great scholar, Vishnu Sharma, blessed the princes and said, "May there always be rift in the houses of your enemies, may the wicked persons be destroyed by the law of nature, may your subjects be always happy in your kingdom and may the children always enjoy the garden of the stories of ethics of Hitopadesh.

❏ ❏

# VIGRAHA

'There is great strength in unity,' and this is Law of Nature. Energy flowing in one particular direction becomes weak if obstructed. You must be aware that breaking one stick at a time is possible, but breaking a faggot, when the sticks are bundled up, is impossible. Where, on the one side, unity is a powerful means of achieving victory over one's enemy, on the other side, not being organized in oneself would make one weak, and one will have to accept defeat.

# 1

## ONCE THERE WAS A HERON

Once there lived a male swan in Karpoor island on the bank of river Padmakeli. His name was Hiranygarbha.

A heron happened to arrive there. His name was Deerghamukha.

"Hello, brother Deerghamukha! How are you? How did you happen to come here?" said the male swan to the heron.

"King! Are we expected to become silent listeners to criticism of our king from foreigners?"

"No, brother! No true patriot will tolerate this kind of a thing."

"King! Similarly when I too could not tolerate criticism of my king, I rebounded in the same language and, with the result, one who was criticising my king, came down to the level of fighting with me."

Hiranyagarbha understood that the heron had done something in the neighbouring kingdom which would not be in his favour.

The heron narrating his story—"There is a huge mountain, named Vindhya, in Jambu island. A peacock, named Mayur Raj is the king of that island. One day his soldiers saw me there wandering about and arrested me. They began interrogating me, asking—'Who are you? Where have you come from?"

"I told them that I was a subject of the kingdom of Hiranyagarbha, and was wandering about in Jambu island without any special purpose. Hearing me the minister of the king said—'Brother! You have seen your country and now you have seen our country as well. Now tell me which kingdom is better of the two. Also please tell us which of the two kings is greater and more knowledgeable."

"I told him that our kingdom is no less than heaven itself. You people are only wasting away your life living in this island. I shall show you the kingdom in which I live if you accompany me. Our kingdom is like heaven and our king is no less than Lord Indra himself."

"The moment I said this they became terribly angry with me. And this was very natural also. The scholars say that feeding milk to a serpent is like making him more venomous and, giving sermons to a person who is mentally derailed is like giving rise to his madness. It is necessary for the wise to give sermons only to those who are suitable for it.

"Once this kind of sermon was given by some birds to monkeys and with the result the birds were compelled to leave their homes."

"How did that happen?" asked Hiranyagarbha in a surprised tone.

"Listen! I am going to tell you the story of those foolish monkeys," said Deerghamukha.

# 2

# FOOLISH MONKEYS

There was a huge silk-cotton tree on the bank of river Narmada.

A large number of birds lived happily in their nests in that tree.

There flowed a river near this tree, and the birds and the passers-by drank water from it to quench their thirst. Also the passers-by would stop and relax in the cool shade of this tree.

One day a group of monkeys happened to arrive there all of a sudden. And before the monkeys could return it suddenly began raining cats and dogs.

For safety from the rains the birds crouched in their nests, whereas the monkeys remained outside in the open crouched among the foliage. It was not possible for them to go anywhere. There bodies began shivering due to extreme cold.

The king of birds was filled with pity to see the helpless monkeys; but at the same time he was filled with anger, thinking—'God has given them two hands, but these monkeys, instead of building homes for themselves, keep themselves busy in destructive activities only.'

Thinking all this he said to the monkeys, "O brothers! You are all clever and capable, but I fail to understand as to why you have not been able to build homes for yourselves as yet. We are nothing before you, but see how comfortably we are sitting in our homes."

Truth is generally unpleasant.

And so was the case with the monkeys. They became extremely angry to hear him speak thus.

In fact what the king of birds said was mere truth and was in good sense. But the monkeys could not welcome it. They thought that the king of birds was trying to make fun of them. They thought—'These birds have seen monkeys only till date; they have not seen their wisdom and anger.'

In order to exact revenge on birds the monkeys swung into action as soon as the rain stopped. Filled with anger they began devastating the nests of the birds.

"What happened next?" asked Hiranyagarbha.

"O king! What worse could have happened? There was lamentation all around. Poor birds became homeless. Why did this happen? Just because the king of birds gave a genuine advice to the monkeys. And ever since I have been telling everyone—'Never give sermons to anyone.' I too made the same mistake of telling Mayur Raj that he should abandon the dry mountainous land. This was enough to rouse their anger. They all pounced on me as soon as I gave them this advice. It had become absolutely clear to me that those in Jambu island were mad and ignorant creatures. And trying to run away from them would have been cowardly. So, I too prepared myself to fight with them. Death was before me with its jaws open to devour me. But trying to run away was no remedy. It is always better to fight bravely and die than dying like a coward."

Hearing this Hiranyagarbha laughed and said, "One who enters into a combat with his enemy without evaluating his physical might or infirmity, is often ridiculed by them. Wise are those who evaluate the might of their enemy before coming to grips with them. And those who fail to do so, are subjected to defeat. Have you heard the story of the donkey who used to graze in fields covered under the hide of a lion, and was killed due to one simple mistake made by him?"

"How?"

"Listen!"

# 3

# THE DONKEY IN THE GUISE OF A LION

There lived a washerman, named Vilas, in Hastinapur. He had a donkey. Vilas would never give him sufficient fodder to eat.

With the result the donkey was losing his weight day by day. Vilas thought—'This donkey is losing its weight, and now, if I didn't make proper arrangements for his fodder, he would die quite soon.'

Suddenly he hit upon a new idea.

Next day the washerman went to a hunter and bought the hide of a lion from him. He covered his donkey under the hide of the lion in the night and drove him out of his house.

This worked like magic for the donkey. He would go to fields, full of crops, during night hours and eat his fill without any fear for anyone.

And thus, not only that the donkey gained his lost weight, but also became healthier.

The farmers would run for safety of their lives to see him in the fields. They always took him to be a lion. The donkey in the guise of a lion had devastated the crops in the fields of those farmers. One poor farmer, seeing his entire growth of crops ruined by the lion, became very sad and thought to himself—'I have no alternative but to kill this lion. If I am destined to die, why die of starvation; why not die fighting with this lion.'

He wore a blanket of dusky colour that night and hiding his bow and arrow in it, sat in a corner in his field. The donkey came in the night and, seeing the farmer covered under a dusky blanket, thought he too was a donkey like him. Forgetting that he was in the guise of a lion he began braying loudly.

As soon as the farmer heard him braying it became clear to him that the creature in the field was not a lion but a donkey. "I am not going to spare his life now," murmured the farmer to himself.

The farmer poised an arrow on the bowstring and released it to find its mark in the direction of the donkey. The donkey in the guise of lion died on the spot.

"Brother Deerghamukha! This is the reason why I say that it is a great vice not to evaluate the might of others. Failing to do so may bring an end to one's life any moment," said Hiranyagarbha, "anyway, now please tell me what happened to you next in that island."

"King! As soon as I spoke in praise of our kingdom and our people, they all pounced on me, saying—'right now you are on our land and you dare criticise us and our king. This is something we can never tolerate.' They were all pecking at me and injuring me, and saying—'Your king is very soft-hearted, but remember, mere softness of heart doesn't help protect a kings rights. Sometimes the soft-hearted ones can't even protect the money in their hands.'

"People would be scared of only hearing the name of a king who is known for his valour. Many things can be managed only in his name, like the rabbits managed things in the name of the moon and lived comfortably."

"How?" I asked the birds of that island.

The birds said, "Listen! O wicked heron! We shall tell you the story."

# 4

# A RUSE

Once the entire forest area of Kashipuram was hit by drought. What to talk of human beings, even animals in the forest began running away to distant places in search of water.

There was complete chaos all around.

All the living beings began dying of thirst.

The human beings as well as wild animals would start running in the direction in which they hoped to get some water.

A large number of elephants lived on the bank of a river in Kashipuram forest.

Their chief's name was Karna.

The families of these elephants had been living on the bank of this river for years together. But when the water level began declining in this river also, the elephants began finding it difficult to bathe and drink water from it. Under these circumstances the chief of elephants decided to leave that river and shift to the other nearby river which had ample water for them.

The chief of the elephants took them to that river to show that there was water in abundance in it.

The chief of rabbits was shocked to see the herd of elephants along the bank of the river.

From that day onwards the elephants began enjoying their time. They would bathe in it, drink water from it and play happily. The rabbits, for fear of being trampled under the feet of the elephants, would be seen sitting in a corner, keeping themselves at a safe distance. They had no alternative either.

The same night the rabbits convened an emergeny meeting in order to find some way to get rid of the problem. They knew it only too well that it was impossible for them to counter the might of the huge elephants. The only alternative was to apply their wits.

The chief of rabbits said, "Friends! Applying our wits is the only possible way. Once a rabbit, who was one of us, had killed a lion. And now you will see how I chase away these elephants from here."

All the rabbits were looking at their chief wide-eyed, not knowing anything about his plans.

Next day in the early morning the chief of rabbits went and met the chief of elephants and said very patiently, "O king of elephants! May I know the purpose of your visit to this place?"

"Who are you to ask this question to me?"

"I am a rabbit, a messenger of the Moon god, and am under the instructions of Lord Indra to come and see you."

"Why has the Moon god sent you to me?"

"He is of the view that you elephants have committed a lot of sins."

"We have committed sins...How can to you say that?"

"Look, O king of elephants! All of you drink water from this river, and at the same time you make the water dirty by bathing in it. Personally

I am of the view that the anger of the Moon is going to be disastrous for you."

"You rabbit! You are trying to fool us. We have not even seen the moon you are talking about."

"If that be so, please come alone tonight and I shall show you the moon."

"Coming alone will not be possible."

"But why?"

"Because it's not only I who would like to see the Moon god; I would like all my friends also to join me. This would give a meaning to our lives."

The rabbit came along with the elephants to the bank of the river and stood there with them. It was full moon night, and the image of the moon could be clearly seen in the water of the river.

"O king of elephants! Look into the river. The Moon god is clearly visible in it. Now I shall tell him about you all," and saying this the rabbit bowed before the river and began muttering with his hands joined together, "O Moon god! Look, the king of elephants and his friends have come here to apologize for having made the mistake of making the water of this river dirty. O god! Please extend your forgiveness."

The clever rabbit continued muttering thus, and the elephants, terror-stricken, were standing there with their heads bowed down.

Just then the rabbit said to the king of elephants, "O king of elephants! Please open your eyes and see the Moon god in the river water."

The elephants began looking into the river. The image of the bright moon was clearly visible in it. All the elephants began bowing their heads with reverence and offering salutations to Moon god.

The king of elephants said, "O god! We sincerely apologize for our mistake and promise that never in future shall we make the water of this river dirty."

And after this the elephants left the place and went away.

Having narrated the story the birds said, "This is the reason why we say that even the toughest of jobs can be done by using names of the powerful ones."

After hearing this story from them I said, "Our king is very powerful and capable. He is Lord of all the three worlds; what to talk of this kingdom."

Then the birds said, "O you wicked bird! If that be so, why is it that you are wandering about on our land?"

They took me to their king, Chitravarna and, after offering their salutations to him, they said, "O king! This heron lives in our country and casts aspersions on you."

Hearing this the king said, "Who is he and where has he come from?"

"King! He is the servant of King Hiranyagarbha of Karpoor island."

Then his minister, who was a vulture, said, "Who is the Chief Minister there?"

I said, "Our Chief Minister is a ruddy-goose who has the knowledge of all the treatises."

Then a parrot said, "O king! Karpoor island is one among the other small islands of Jambu island. Karpoor island comes in your territory."

Then the king said, "Yes, yes, why not! Kings, mad people, lascivious women and egotists always strive for unobtainable things. Things, easily obtainable, do not interest them."

Hearing this I said, "If it had been that simple that one would wish and get a kingdom, Jambu island would have been the kingdom of our king, Hiranyagarbha. This is possible only after winning a war."

"All right!" said the king of Jambu island, "Go and tell your king to make preparations for war."

I said, "You may please send your messenger."

They debated over this issue and finally came to the conclusion that the parrot would be the fittest creature to be sent as messenger.

At this the parrot said, "As you wish, O Lord! But this heron is a wicked creature. I shall not go with him. One should always avoid being in the company of such creatures. Because once a swan and a pheasant had to lose their lives for being in the company of a crow."

"How so?" asked the king.

Then the parrot said, "Listen, I am telling you the story."

❏ ❏

# 5

# AVOID THE COMPANY OF
# THE WICKED ONES

There lived a crow in a Peepal tree in Ujjaini town. And there also lived a swan in a nearby river. Both were temperamentally unsuited to each other. The swan was truthful and kind-hearted, whereas the crow was equally wicked and sinful.

During summers a passer-by happened to arrive there. Since he was extremely tired, he decided to take rest in the cool shade of the tree. Putting his bow and arrows by his side he slept under the tree.

He slept comfortably for quite some time but when the sun moved toward the west, the rays began falling directly on his face. Seeing this the swan spread his wings to save the passer-by from the hot rays of the sun.

The passer-by was deep asleep with his mouth open. Seeing the swan providing shade to the passer-by with his wings spread across, the crow said, "Brother! Why is it that you are taking so much trouble for this passer-by? Are you not aware that these human beings are our real enemies?"

"Brother! All beings are not alike. We should always consider the virtues of others and not the vices."

"Nonsense! We too should teach them a lesson for the kind of tortures they subject us to. Just see what I am going to do to him," saying this the crow defecated on the face of the passer-by and flew away from there. The passer-by woke up and began looking up angrily.

The crow had done his job and flown away, but the poor swan remained sitting there. The passer-by took the swan to have defecated on him. He poised an arrow on his bowstring angrily and shot it at the swan. The poor swan, hit by the arrow, fell dead.

"O king! Such is this world. Being in bad company never yields good results. Now I shall tell you the story of a pheasant," saying this the parrot began narrating the other story.

❏ ❏

# 6

# BAD COMPANY YIELDS BAD RESULTS

There lived a crow and a pheasant in a tree. Once the birds came to know that their king, Lord Garuda, was going to arrive at the seashore. All the birds moved toward the sea to have a glimpse of their king, Lord Garuda. The crow and the pheasant were no less excited about it. They too had a great desire to see him.

While on their way to the seashore they happened to see a cowherd going with a pitcher full of yoghurt on his head. The crow's mouth filled with water to see the yoghurt. And forgetting the main purpose of his errand he came flying down and landed on the pitcher.

Sitting comfortably on the pitcher he began eating the yoghurt. The cowherd also noticed that someone was eating yoghurt from his pitcher. Crows are very cunning. Instead of sitting continuously and eating from the pitcher the crow would take a little of yoghurt in his beak and fly away. Then again he would come, sit on the pitcher, take a little of yoghurt in his beak and again fly away. Thus, the cowherd continued moving and the crow continued eating from his pitcher. The pheasant tried to check the crow from doing so, but the crow didn't listen to him.

The cowherd tried to catch the crow while still proceeding on his way, but when he could not, he put down the pitcher of yoghurt on the ground and hid himself in a corner waiting for the thief of yoghurt to come. He looked up and saw a crow and a pheasant sitting on a branch of a tree.

The cowherd understood that those two birds were the thieves of the yoghurt. Out of anger he picked up a stone lying nearby and threw it in the direction of the birds. But the moment the cowherd had picked up the stone, the cunning crow had understood that the cowherd was going to hit them. And the crow flew away; but poor pheasant, who was innocent, remained sitting there. The stone thrown by the cowherd came whizzing and hit the pheasant. The pheasant whined with pain and fell on the ground. While breathing his last he said, "O sinful crow! You got me killed for no fault of mine."

"This is the result of keeping a bad company, O king! This is the reason why I say that I shall not go with this heron," said the parrot.

Hearing the heron speak thus, I said, "Why do you talk in this manner. For me you and my king are one and the same."

Then the parrot said, "Listen to me, O king! No matter how sweet the wicked ones may sound, they create as much fear as the human beings do. O heron! Your wickedness becomes clear from the very fact that your statements have become instrumental in instigating a war between two kings. Fools can be fooled by talking sweetly despite a crime committed before their eyes. Like a carpenter who, hearing his wife talk sweetly, hoisted her lover on his shoulders and began dancing happily.

"How did that happen?" asked the king.

"Listen, O king! I am telling you the story."

# 7

# FALSE PRAISE

There lived a carpenter in Youvanshri town. His name was Budhram. Budhram was very hard working. He would work day and night to earn the bread and butter for his family. In fact Budhram was very simple and nice. But his wife was very cunning. Her name was Kali.

Kali didn't like her husband. The reason behind this was that her husband would leave home early in the morning and return late in the night. Passing her time in isolation used to become very difficult for her. And in order to counter her problem of isolation she made friends with another man. The moment the carpenter would leave home, her lover would come to give company to her. Being together used to be real fun for them.

Gradually the development of illicit relations between Kali and her lover became a talk of the town, and Budhram also came to know about it. Coming to know of the infidelity of his wife made Budhram very sad. But he didn't think it proper to take action against his wife on the basis of hearsay only. He thought that it was not proper for him to say anything unless he caught them red-handed. He was waiting for an opportune time.

One day Budhram said to his wife that he was going out of town for some important work, and would return after two or three days. Hearing this Kali became very happy, thinking that she would be absolutely free for two-three days and enjoy her time with her lover.

Kali went and called her lover as soon as Budhram left home.

In fact Budhram didn't have to go anywhere. It was only part of his plan in order to be able to catch his wife red-handed. And so, as soon as his wife went out to call her lover, Budhram came and hid himself under the bed in the room.

While Kali was lying in bed with her lover and enjoying her time, she very unmindfully hung her hand and happened to touch the face of Budhram who was hiding under the bed.

Kali was quick to understand that there was something wrong, and that it was perhaps her husband hiding under the bed.

Now the situation had become alarming. She thought—'I shall be nowhere if my husband catches me red-handed. Kali's brain used to start working very fast under such circumstances. She was cleverer than her husband. So she began enacting a drama to counter her husband.

She began telling her lover—

"I have brought you here to inquire from you as to why you keep casting aspersions on my god-like husband. I don't even know whether my god-like husband, who is on a tour away from his town, has eaten anything or not. I am greatly worried about him."

"You love Budhram so much?" asked Kali's lover in a surprised tone.

"You can never know about love between a husband and a wife. Listen is you want to know—

"A woman who, despite every kind of harshness from her husband's side, goes to her husband happily, is considered very fortunate. No matter what kind of husband a man is, he is like a god to his wife."

"Kali you are talking very strange today," Kali's lover was getting shocks after shocks to see her in an absolutely changed form.

"I am talking about the duties of a truthful and sincere wife. Only a wife knows what the status of a husband is. What are you? You are simply an idle loafer. I always worship my husband in the manner like someone would worship God. Perhaps you are not aware that a man has three and half crore hairs on his body. And a wife who willingly burns herself on her husband's funeral pyre, gets a span of three and half crore years in heaven. And now you yourself tell me why should I not remain a chaste woman."

Hearing his wife speak thus Budhram became very happy. He, out of extreme happiness, lifted the cot from below and, hoisting it above his head, began dancing and saying—"How fortunate I am to be a husband of a chaste and sweet-tongued woman."

Having narrated the story the parrot said, "This is the reason why I say that sometimes a person, even after seeing the biggest crimes being committed before his eyes, proves to be a big fool just because he has been talked sweetly. The greatest of sins become microscopic when talked sweetly. So, a person should not become happy to hear his false praise."

Subsequently the king bade us farewell after observing their traditional rites. The parrot, his messenger, is on the way to your kingdom. He would be arriving any moment. And so, please do whatever is needful.

Hearing the heron, the ruddy-goose who was the minister of Hiranyagarbha, spoke sarcastically—"O king! As far as possible, the heron has performed his royal duties on a foreign land. But this is the difference between a man of wisdom and a fool. A man of wisdom would not allow an altercation to take place under any circumstance, and a fool would create circumstances out of nothing, so that an altercation takes place."

On this Hiranyagarbha said, "Well, what is done cannot be undone. It's no use apportioning blames now. Now we have to contemplate countering the situation. Think about it and find some way."

"Lord! I feel it's demand of time that I should render my views in isolation only," said the ruddy-goose, "because even if a secret is whispered in the ear, the others standing around may make something out of it just by observing the countenance of the speaker and the listener. Therefore, anything secret must be discussed in isolation."

Hiranyagarbha ordered everyone present there to disperse. Only Hiranyagarbha and the ruddy-goose remained there.

The ruddy-goose said, "It seems the heron has created these circumstances under someone's instigation only."

"Look, we shall look into the reason later. Right now I want you to advise me and come out with a solution to the problem," said Hiranyagarbha.

"Lord! First we shall have to send a spy to evaluate the power of our enemy king. This will help us know where he stands. A king without a spy is considered blind. It is through spies that a king gathers knowledge about good and bad deeds and the tactics of an enemy king. Send someone whom you trust along with your spy. Your spy shall be required to remain there and send secret information through your trusted man. A successful spy would be one who is an amphibian. I would advise you to send the heron as your spy. He may be accompanied by some other heron. Our plans should remain a top secret."

Hiranyagarbha, after thinking for some time, said, "Well, we have a capable spy."

"Then in that case victory is ours," said the ruddy-goose.

Just then Hiranyagarbha's aide to the door came and informed that a parrot, who was a messenger from Jambu island, had come.

The ruddy-goose said, "Take him to the royal guest house and make his stay comfortable."

"As you wish," said the aide to the door and proceeded to escort the parrot to the royal guest house.

Hiranyagarbha said, "It seems the war may break any time."

"Lord!" said the ruddy-goose, "I don't think this is time when we should declare war. It is advisable to evaluate the might of the enemy and make suitable arrangements for the fortification of the fort before declaring a war on the enemy. Apart from all this, there should be sufficient number of weapons and enough provisions for our army in the fort."

"You yourself suggest to me as to who should be appointed for the fortification of the fort."

"I would suggest to you to appoint the stork for this job," said the ruddy-goose.

Hiranyagarbha immediately sent for the stork. He ordered him to proceed with the fortification of the fort at the earliest.

Meanwhile the aid to the door came again and said, "Lord! A crow has come along with his family from Sinhal island and is sitting at the entrance. He wishes to see you."

"In my view crows are intelligent and witty. It will be in favour of us if he is on our side," said Hiranyagarbha.

"There is no dispute in what you say, O king! But it seems he is a spy of our enemy. O king! One who abandons his friends and exhibits his love for his enemy, meets his end like the blue jackal did."

"Who was that blue jackal?"

"Listen please! I shall tell you the story of the blue jackal."

Once a jackal struck by hunger set out to some village. Having starved for many days in the forest he had decided to move to some village in search of food.

As soon as he entered the village, the dogs of the village began chasing him and barking at him.

Seeing the dogs so badly after him, he began running for safety of his life; and in this process he entered the house of a dyer. The dyer had prepared a mixture of blue colour in a vessel of clay for dyeing clothes.

In sheer perplexity and nervousness the jackal fell in the vessel.

With the result his colour changed. Now he was absolutely blue in colour. And the dogs, not able to find the jackal, returned disappointed. After some time the jackal came out of the vessel and began wandering around in search of food in the house. He found a few stale pieces of bread in a corner. The jackal ate it and was satisfied to have had something to fight starvation.

Having eaten his fill the jackal moved back to the forest. The village dogs saw him and were terribly scared to see a new kind of animal in blue colour. They scampered away out of fear.

The jackal was totally confused. He was not able to understand as to why the dogs, who were after his blood, were so terribly scared. Then he suddenly noticed the change in the colour of his body and everything became absolutely clear to him. He could understand that it was the change in the colour of his body that had made the difference. He began thinking—"Now the animals in the forest also will be afraid of me." He was very happy now.

The other jackals were shocked to see him when he entered the forest. They began saying—"Brother! What has happened to you?"

"Brothers!" said the jackal applying his wits, "I had gone out to the temple of the goddess of forests and I kept worshipping her throughout the night standing on one foot. Pleased with my worships, the goddess appeared to me and granted me kingship of the forest. And it is precisely for this reason that she has changed my colour."

Coming to know that the goddess of the forests had declared the blue jackal the king of the forest, the other jackals became very happy and began shouting slogans of victory. Seeing the jackals shouting slogans of victory the other animals also joined them. And what to talk of small animals, even big animals like wolves, tigers and lions followed suit.

And thus, that blue jackal became the king of entire forest. Now the jackals of the forest had an upper hand. All the animals, small and big, offered salutations to the blue jackal with great reverence. The animals would queue up outside the palace everyday to find favour in the eyes of the blue jackal. It was the same jackal who was dying of starvation in the forest a few days ago, and now the position was that he had a number of servants to arrange the best possible meals for him. Even the lions and wolves would arrange tasty flesh for him to eat. And within a few days he was a different creature in perfect health.

It was for the first time in the history of forests that a jackal had become a king. But after some time the other jackals began noticing a definite change in the behaviour of the blue jackal. He, instead of giving importance to his own species, began giving importance to animals of other species. The other jackals took it as a great insult for themselves. They called for a meeting which was headed by an old jackal. The old jackal stood up and said, "Brothers! I understand your pain. Please don't worry. I know this jackal has ignored his own species. He doesn't care for us. We shall definitely exact a revenge on him."

"But how is it possible for us to exact a revenge on him when we know that even fierce animals like lions and tigers have become his slaves. The elephants and wolves too have accepted him as their king. They are all shouting slogans of victory for him."

"Yes, yes, I know everything. And this is the greatest foolishness of that foolish jackal that he, ignoring his own species, has begun favouring the other species of animals. That fool hates us now. And his this very attitude is going to determine his fate. We must expose him now."

"But how shall we make it possible?"

"We shall hide ourselves in the bushes around his palace tonight. And as soon as he comes out of his palace we shall start howling in unison. This will certainly give rise to his natural instincts, and he too will start howling with us. The moment he starts howling, all the animals in this forest will understand that he is nothing more than an ordinary jackal. He will be completely exposed thus."

All the jackals agreed with the old jackal. They began howling, dancing and jumping around when the night fell.

Hearing the jackals howling, the blue jackal forgot that he was the king of the forest. He came out of his palace and began howling and dancing along with the other jackals.

As soon as the lion saw the blue jackal in his original form he immediately understood that the blue jackal was a cheat and had become their king by adopting deceptive methods. The lion thought— "All right, you cheat! We shall teach you a lesson."

"Catch hold of this cheat. Don't let him go. Kill him," saying this the lion and other animals of the forest began chasing him.

And it took the fierce animals of the forest no time to kill the blue jackal and within moments pieces of his body were seen strewn around in the forest.

Having narrated the story the ruddy-goose said, "O king! How far could someone, who has left his own clan and come on our side, be trusted?"

"Well, what you say is correct," said Hiranyagarbha, "but right now he is our guest. A guest, who has come from a distant place, must be extended hearty welcome. Anyway...let him settle down comfortably here. We shall think about it later."

And then, at the orders of Hiranyagarbha, the crow was called in.

Meanwhile, the stork came and said, "O king! The fort has been constructed and also a messenger has been sent there."

"All right, we should let the parrot come in now," said the ruddy-goose.

The parrot came in and offered his salutations with humbleness, but spoke with a little of haughtiness, "O Hiranyagarbha! I am a messenger of my king, Chitravarna. My king has ordered me to convey to you that you must go and fall in his feet if you at all care for your kingdom and your life. Or else he must leave his kingdom and go to some other place."

"Stop talking nonsense. Or else I shall feel compelled to deprive you of your sharp tongue," said Hiranyagarbha in a paroxysm of anger.

"King! Kindly allow me to chop off the tongue of this parrot so that he realizes what punishment one deserves for inflicting insults on the king of our country," said the crow angrily.

"No our code of ethics doesn't allow this. It says—"No matter how a messenger behaves, he must be honoured," said the ruddy-goose contradicting the crow.

The ruddy-goose gave away gifts in the form of gold and gems and said to him while bidding him farewell—"Brother! Go and tell your king that we are in no way interested in any kind of war, but we welcome it if imposed on us. We are fully prepared."

The parrot returned to his king, Mayur, and narrated the whole sequence of happenings to him. Having been detailed thoroughly the king called for an emergeny meeting. He made everyone in the meeting aware of the situation and said, "Now please think all of you and tell me what we should do to gain victory."

The far-sighted vulture stood up and said, "King! It is not advisably to attack the enemy without giving a serious thought to it. If a king is not careful about it he may have to face the blade of the sword of his enemy. Now I am going to tell you something about the ethics of war—

Rivers and mountains are places where an attacking king is expected to form a maze of his army, because these are places which are most risky. A king should have ample money also during such hours of crisis. And one must not engage oneself into war without deciding a definite policy."

"All right, I understand what you mean. Please send for the royal astrologer and ask him to make calculations to find an auspicious day to begin the war," Mayur, the king, announced his orders and now everyone had to obey his command.

Within a period of twenty-four hours King Mayur launched an attack on the kingdom of Hiranyagarbha. The attack was so powerful that for a moment Hiranyagarbha got totally perplexed. He never expected King Mayur to launch an attack all of a sudden. And the army of King Mayur was attacking definite quarters of the kingdom of Hiranyagarbha in such a manner and with such precision as if they were aware of every nook and corner of the neighbouring kingdom.

Hiranyagarbha called on his home minister and asked, "Who is the traitor in our country who is providing help to our enemy? Who has disclosed all the secrets of our country to King Mayur?"

"King! I have my doubts on the crow! He is the only outsider in our country."

"But this crow was the first one who had come forward to kill the parrot."

"King! That was only a ruse which you could not understand. Every spy enacts this kind of drama to win the trust of the enemy. Right now I can only tell you that one who acts without thinking has to face the consequences that a greedy barber had to."

"I couldn't quite follow what you said," said Hiranyagarbha with his eyes fixed on his minister.

"Listen, I am going to tell you the story of a foolish barber, who, out of greed, lost everything," saying this the ruddy-goose began narrating the story.

❏ ❏

# 8

# GREEDY BARBER

There lived a man named Choodamani in Ayodhya town. He always discoursed on philosophy and religion among the people of Ayodhya. Since he was a worshipper of Mother Saraswati, he was deprived of the kind blessings of Mother Lakshmi. And this was the reason why Choodamani had no money. He was very poor.

Just as Choodamani was coming out of a temple, one day, after offering his worships he happened to meet a saint. He immediately offered his salutations and touched his feet.

"Be happy, O devotee," said the saint showering his blessings on Choodamani.

"Maharaj! I despite being a devotee of God, am very poor. And this poverty has made my life very sad. Is there anything that you can do so that I could lead a happy life?"

"My child! You must worship Lord Shiva if you wish to attain happiness in your life. You shall have to observe fast and offer water to Shivalingam for forty continuous days. Lord Shiva will give you everything that you will wish," saying this the saint left.

Choodamani, as per the instructions of the saint, began observing fast and pouring water on Shivalingam very religiously.

And thus, after completion of forty days of worship, Lord Shiva appeared to Choodamani in his dream and said, "My child! You have succeeded in pleasing me through your worship. Now go home, get a hair-cut, take bath and put on new clothes; and stand behind your house with a staff in your hand. A beggar will come begging at your door. All that you have to do is that you strike his head with your staff as soon as he asks for alms. He will die. And as soon as he dies, you should touch his head with your hand while repeating my name. Then you will see a miracle happening. His body well be transformed completely into gold. And that quantity of gold will be sufficient for your whole life," saying this in his dream Lord Shiva disappeared.

Next day Choodamani got up early in the morning, got a hair-cut, bathed himself properly, put on new clothes, and went and stood behind his house with a staff in his hand. After some time a beggar came begging for alms at his door. And Choodamani did as directed by Lord Shiva. He struck the head of the beggar with his staff. The beggar fell dead on the spot. Choodamani, while repeating the name of Lord Shiva, touched the head of the beggar with his hand, and the body of the beggar was immediately transformed into gold.

"Great are you, O Lord Shiva! You have filled my life with every happiness," saying this Choodamani began dancing happily.

There was a barber who lived adjacent to Choodamani's house. He was watching the scene from there. With a glint of greed in his eyes he decided to repeat the act.

And on the next day the barber too did the same thing, thinking that that was the easiest method of filling one's life with happiness. He thought that with such quantity of gold he would be able to sit and eat all his life without having to do anything. He began imagining that he would get a huge mansion built for himself and would live in it, not as Kartara barber, but as Seth Kartar Chand. People would call him from outside—"Is Seth Ji available?"

Imagining thus, the beggar went and stood behind his house on the next day with a staff in his hand. And as soon as a beggar came begging for alms at his door, the barber struck the head of the beggar with his staff applying all his strength.

The barber had struck the beggar with such force that the beggar died on the spot. Kartar touched the head of the beggar thinking that a miracle would take place and the beggar's body would be transformed into gold.

The barber waited for a long time, sitting there, hoping some miracle to take place, but to no avail. On the contrary some soldiers came there and, seeing the dead body of the beggar and the barber sitting there, arrested him.

The king gave a hearing to the case and ultimately announced his judgement awarding the barber with capital punishment.

Having narrated the story of the greedy barber the ruddy-goose said, "O king! This is the result of greed and foolishness.

"But how are we going to get the secrets of King Mayur?"

"Please don't worry about it. Just now I have been informed by my spies that King Mayur has exiled the vulture, who was his minister. O king! Please always remember that an enemy's enemy is always a friend. Now we shall make friends with the vulture and extract all the secrets of our enemy from him."

"Do you think that he would agree to become our friend?"

"King! This is very natural. Where will a minister go after being exiled with such insult? He can go in the shelter of some king only. We shall have double advantage of his exile. One is that our enemy king will become weak, and the other advantage will be that we shall get all the vital secrets of the enemy king from the exiled minister. And so, I am of the view that taking advantage of the present circumstances, we should launch a heavy attack on our enemy king. This is an opportune time."

Seeing the genuineness in the argument of his minister,

Hiranyagarbha launched a heavy attack on the enemy king.

King Mayur was already facing problems of internal feuds; and having exiled his intelligent and far-sighted minister he had become too weak. And, above all, the heavy attack launched by the army of Hiranyagarbha, crushed him and made him all the more weak. Ultimately King Mayur had to make an unconditional surrender before Hiranyagarbha. And as soon as he surrendered, his old minister, the vulture, came before him wearing a broad smile on his face.

"Hello king! How was that?"

"Oh, you have come here to laugh at my downfall," said King Mayur to the vulture.

"King! You yourself are responsible for your downfall. I had already explained to you the ethics of politics. But, instead of trying to follow my advice, you chose to attack your enemy without giving a serious thought to it. King! Statecraft lays that one should not lose the sense of logic in one's zeal to do something. No matter how huge and brave an army is, if made to fight without observing the code of ethics, it shall meet its own doom."

"Now I realize my folly. I admit that it was a grave mistake on my part to have exiled you. I have also been sufficiently punished for my mistake. Now I request you to return and take charge of your seat once again, and get me out of this terrible situation."

The vulture's heart melted to see King Mayur repentant and ashamed of his deed. He said, "O King Mayur! It's no use weeping and wailing now. What is done cannot be undone. But once again I am at your service."

"O minister! Our country is being plundered. My army is fast losing its self-confidence. What to do now?"

"O King! Please don't worry. I shall reunite the remaining army, create confidence in the hearts of our soldiers and launch an attack on our enemy in the night itself. But I need your kind permission for this."

"You are my minister. Do whatever you deem fit. And you need not wait for my permission for this."

The vulture reunited the remaining army of King Mayur and proceeded with it to besiege the fort of Hiranyagarbha.

# SANDHI

It is also very important to know as to with whom one should associate oneself. One must associate oneself with those having common targets. But one must be careful to see that he does not jeopardize his own existence by associating himself with someone. It is always favourable to strike a compromise deal with someone more powerful than oneself. The wise observe a compromise and strife, both at the same time. It is only under compelling circumstances that one gets into compromise with someone, whereas, a strife is nothing but an expressive effort to get out of such circumstances. A compromise doesn't mean that one should become carefree.

# 1

# COMPROMISE

On the other side the spies of Hiranyagarbha came and informed him that King Mayur was coming with his remaining army to besiege his fort.

Hiranyagarbha was aware of the fact that King Mayur was not as powerful as he was earlier; but since the vulture had once again joined hands with his king, King Mayur had regained his power to quite an extent.

Hiranyagarbha was lost in thoughts. His army too didn't have the zeal it had earlier. The entire army was busy celebrating their victory. And busy in their merry-making the soldiers of Hiranyagarbha's army didn't even know that the army of King Mayur had besieged their fort.

The soldiers in the fort of Hiranyagarbha dived into the river for safety of their lives. They had no alternative either.

At such hour of crisis the stork came forward to defend Hiranyagarbha from the enemy. But it was too late. Hiranyagarbha had already been surrounded by the army of roosters of the enemy king.

The stork said, "Halt! I cannot allow you to kill my king."

Hiranyagarbha said, "O stork! Why are you adamant to sacrifice your life for me?"

"King! Please don't worry. So long as I am alive, neither you will have to face defeat nor can anyone on earth kill you. After all this fort was built by me; and now it is only on my dead body that anyone can go through the door of this fort."

"But why are you risking your life?"

"King! Do you think I shall run away for safety of my life? Do you think if I go away from this place, I shall remain safe from death? One is sure to die, no matter where he goes. And dying fighting for the right cause is sure way to attain martyrdom. And this kind of death is preferable. It's quite possible that our valiance may help us win our lost battle. The greatest of the sins is to leave one's master in the jaws of death and run away like a coward."

Just then a rooster came and pecked at the body of Hiranyagarbha. Hiranyagarbha fell into the river and survived but poor stork attained martyrdom fighting bravely. This cleared the way of the army of King Mayur. They began celebrating their victory.

But at such hour when they were celebrating their victory, the remaining army of Hiranyagarbha was reuniting and preparing to launch a fresh attack. And just then the ruddy-goose came forward for a compromise deal. Both the parties agreed to compromise with each other.

Hiranyagarbha asked his minister, "Who was it who set fire to my fort?"

Just then the ruddy-goose came forward and spoke with disappointment, "King! That crow and his family are not to be seen anywhere."

"Now I understand. It was that crow who was the spy of our enemy. It is because of him that I have had to face defeat."

"O king! One must not trust an outsider blindly. I shall tell you the story of an outsider who lost his life owing to his foolishness. Now please listen," said the ruddy-goose.

# 2

# FOOLISH TURTLE

Thousands of animals and birds used to quench their thirst by drinking water from the river Phullotpal in Magadha. On the bank of the river there lived a pair of swans and a turtle.

These three were very pally with each other. The animals and birds would come, drink water from the river and return, but these three would always remain there and pass their time happily talking with each other.

One day some fishermen happened to come toward the river. Seeing a large number of fish in the river they were filled with happiness.

One of the fishermen said, "Fantastic! I had never seen such a large number of fish in any river. Let us cast our nets or else these fish will escape.

The turtle, who was listening to their discussion, began trembling with fear. He went to the pair of swans, his friends, and said—

"O dear friends! Did you hear what these fishermen are talking about?"

"No, we didn't hear, but we are aware that there is something fishy about their presence around this place."

"Dear friends! I am terribly scared. I know you can save your lives by flying away. But what will be my fate?"

"Why are you becoming nervous so much in advance? We shall tackle the situation when the time comes."

"Dear friends! The scholars say that those who keep waiting until the circumstances really become adverse are sure to meet sad ends."

"How so?"

Then the turtle began telling them this story—

❑ ❑

# 3

# RIGHT DECISION AT THE RIGHT MOMENT

Many years ago two fishermen came to this very river to catch fish. During those days three members of our family lived in this river. All the three began trembling with fear to see nets in the hands of those fishermen.

Even the most brave start sweating to see death before them; what to talk of the poor turtles. Two of the turtles became extremely worried about their families and said to the third one—"Friend! Do something. We shall die a prematured death if we didn't do something in time. After all the burden of safety of our kiths and kins is on our shoulders."

The third turtle spoke with carelessness—"We shall see when the time comes. Why should we worry now?"

Seeing the third turtle talking so carelessly, the two turtles became very angry. They discussed the situation among themselves and arrived at the conclusion that they should not be misguided by what the foolish turtle said. They thought that he himself will die putting the safety of his family in jeopardy and will get them also killed. And thinking this the two turtles began preparing to leave that river along with their families. The third turtle muttered to himself—"Cowardly creatures! They are leaving their home unnecessarily. These fishermen have only arrived here. They have not even cast their nets yet, and they are running away for safety of their lives. Being afraid of a happening even before it has happened is nothing but cowardice."

"Keep your ideals with yourself. Let us be cowardly if we are. The scholars say—'One who finds a solution to a problem in time is considered wise. A clever woman had once saved her lover by applying her wisdom at the right moment.'

"And what's that story?"

"Listen! I shall tell you the story."

❑ ❑

# 4

# CRAFTINESS OF A WOMAN

A very long time ago there lived a trader named Samudradatta in Vikrampur town. He had a small shop. His shop was small to see but yielded very good business. And it was due to transactions on a large scale that sometimes Samudradatta had to go out of town also. During his absence, Ratnaprabha, his wife, used to feel very lonely. Since she had no issue it used to bother her all the more.

Once Samudradatta had to remain away from home for a very long time in connection with his business. This made his wife very sad. Loneliness at home bored her to tears. She had a servant named Bansi with whom she used to talk to pass her idle time.

Gradually they began coming close to each other. And a time came when they crossed all the norms of the society without caring for the social stigma.

Now their life had reached such proportions of physical enjoyment that Ratnaprabha would always want that Samudradatta remained away from home. She used to think that a husband who has no time to entertain his wife is of no use. It's only money that concerns him and nothing else in the world. He had forgotten his home and his family life in trying to earn money.

Now Ratnaprabha and Bansi began enjoying their lives thoroughly.

Bansi had become Ratnaprabha's love. One day it so happened that Samudradatta was at home and Ratnaprabha was busy doing something in the kitchen along with Bansi. Suddenly in a frisson of sexual excitement she kissed Bansi. Samudradatta saw her reaching close to the mouth of Bansi, and she too realized that she had been seen by her husband. She immediately clung to a ruse, saying—

"O you son of a thief! See, I have caught you red-handed today. I was wandering as to who was it eating away the cardamoms from my kitchen. Had I not smelled your mouth I would not have known that it were you eating away the cardamoms from my kitchen."

Saying this she said to her husband, "Look dear! Look at this thief. He has been fooling me continuously all these days. It was only in order to catch him red-handed that I had to smell his mouth from so close."

Just then Bansi came and said to Samudradatta—"Look, Seth Ji! A house, in which a mistress is so harsh, is not suitable for a servant. A servant would lose his prestige in a house, the mistress of which goes to the extent of smelling his mouth for cardamoms. I cannot work in your house any more," saying this Bansi began preparing to leave the house. But Samudradatta called him back and said with affection—

"Look, Bansi! She is your mistress. She doesn't like servants who are in a habit of stealing things. Leave this habit. In future, if you need something, you must ask your mistress for it."

"All right, sir! I do sincerely apologize for my mistake. Now if I need anything in future I shall take her permission for it."

"Did you see, O king! How craftily she managed to get herself out of an impossible situation?"

Hearing this story the turtle began saying—"Something that is not to happen, will not happen, and something that has to happen, can in no way be averted."

Saying this both the turtles abandoned the river along with their families. The third turtle remained alone in the river.

The fishermen cast their nets in the river early in the morning. And unfortunately the turtle was caught in the net. But he was very clever. He immediately thought of a ruse to save his life. He pretended dead when the fishermen pulled out the net. The fishermen became very angry to see a dead turtle caught in their net.

They began saying—"He has spoiled our fun. The very first time we have cast our net into this river and have been rewarded with a dead turtle," saying this they threw the turtle back into the river. And as soon as the turtle was thrown back into the river, he began floating in the water happily.

The turtle said to the swans after narrating this story, "Dear friends! Now I would want you two to do something so that my life could be saved. I shall be extremely grateful to you if you took me to some other river."

"What you say is correct, but one who is wise is required to find ways in advance to counter the situations that may invite destruction. Merely running away from a place doesn't solve a problem."

"Friends! You are wasting time unnecessarily. We have hardly any time to waste."

"Brother! Anything done in a hurry always spoils a case, like a heron had to repent for a simple mistake made by him."

"How did that happen?"

"Listen!" and the swan began telling the story.

❏ ❏

# 5

# FAULT OF A HERON

There was a huge Peepal tree in the north, named Gridhrakoot.
Many families of herons lived in that tree.

There also lived a big black serpent in the hollow of the same tree.
As soon as the herons would go away in search of food, the black
serpent would climb up the tree and devour their chicks.

This was something very saddening for the herons. But they were
helpless.

Challenging a serpent was not an ordinary thing.

Ultimately, seeing no way out, the chief of the herons called for a
meeting of herons. They sat together and began thinking of ways to
counter the situation and save their chicks from the serpent.

An old heron said, "Look, it is only a mongoose who can kill this
snake. All that we have to do is to bring some fish from the nearby pond
and put them in a row starting from the hole of the mongoose upto the
hollow of the Peepal tree where the serpent lives. The mongoose will
reach the hollow of the tree eating the fish one by one; and since the
serpents and mongooses are arch-enemies of each other, the
mongoose will kill it and we shall get rid of this wicked creature."

Everyone present there agreed with the old heron. This was the
only way.

All the herons began bringing fish from the pond in the morning and
began putting them in a row starting from the hole of the mongoose and
upto the hollow of the tree.

As soon as the mongoose came out of the hole and saw a number
of fish lying in a row he became very happy. He, along with his family,
began eating the fish happily and thus reached near the hollow of the
tree.

Serpents and mongooses are arch-enemies of each other.

Seeing the serpent the mongooses pounced on him and killed him within no time.

After eating the snake they heard the chicks of herons squeaking from above.

"That's great!" said the mongooses, "First we got fish to eat, then a snake, and now chicks of herons. How lucky we are!"

And within no time, having eaten away the chicks also, they returned.

Now the herons could only be sorry for what they had done.

"This is the result of doing something without considering the pros and cons of it. And this is why we are telling you to think before you act," said the swans to the turtle.

The turtle said to the swans, "Dear friends! Don't worry about me. I think well before I act. I am not a fool that I would do something while in the air that would prove to be detrimental for me. Everyone loves one's life."

The swans realized that the turtle was adamant; and so they went and brought a piece of twig from the forest. Both the swans caught one end each of the twig in their beaks and the turtle caught the twig with his mouth in the middle, and now all the three were flying in the air.

People below began laughing to see them flying in such a manner in the air. This made the turtle very angry and he opened his mouth to say something. And no sooner had he opened his mouth to say something than he came crashing down and dashed against the ground. He died on the spot.

Just then the messenger of Hiranyagarbha came and said, "O king! I had suggested to you to keep an eye on the fort, but you didn't listen to me. In fact the crow, who was a spy of our enemy, was hiding in the fort. It is he who set our fort on fire and escaped from here."

On the other hand King Mayur was extremely pleased with the crow, because it was because of him that he had been able to win the war. The crow, after getting all the secrets of the enemy, had set the fort on fire. King Mayur said to the vulture, "Reward this crow suitably and adorn him with the highest designation at my court. As far as I think, he should be declared the king of the neighbouring kingdom and should be made to replace Hiranyagarbha."

"No, Lord! It's not wise to confer such high status on someone who holds a low status. You must always remember that anyone belonging to lower status harms his own master, if given a higher status, like a mouse did when transformed into a lion by an ascetic.

❏ ❏

# 6

# BAD END

In the hermitage of sage Gautam there lived a sage whose name was Mahatapa. He was a great ascetic. While sage Mahatapa would be busy singing in the praise of God, a mouse would come and listen to his songs quietly with great devotion. One day sage Mahatapa was filled with kindness to see the devotion in a creature like a mouse. He thought that the mouse was such tiny creature that he always had a threat to his life from the other larger creatures, and decided to bring an end to his plight so that he could live with his head high.

Sage Mahatapa was a great devotee of God, and so he was endowed with such spiritual and supernatural powers that anything said by him would come true. In order to bring an end to the plight of the mouse, sage Mahatapa prayed to God to transform the mouse into a lion.

And the next moment the tiny mouse was transformed into a huge lion.

This transformation brought complete change in the mouse. Now, since he had become a lion, he would roam freely and fearlessly in the forests and all the other animals would bow down before him and offer their salutations in his honour. They would shout slogans of victory to him. It was only sage Mahatapa who knew the truth that the lions origin was in a mouse.

The false lion also was aware that it was only sage Mahatapa who was in the knowledge of his real lineage. And this was something that always bothered him. He never wanted anyone to know the real truth, or else there would be no element of fear in the minds of others for him.

One day the false lion thought—'Why not bring an end to the life of the ascetic and end the problem once for all.'

Next day the lion came fully prepared to kill the ascetic; but the ascetic, with his spiritual power, came to know the intentions of the lion. The foolish lion had forgotten that the ascetic who was capable of transforming a mouse into a lion, was also capable of transforming a lion into a mouse.

Sage Mahatapa chanted certain incantations and the lion was once again transformed into the mouse.

Having narrated the story the vulture said, "O King Mayur! It is Nature which has provided this earth with different kinds of species of creatures. Mice, cats, donkeys, horses, elephants, jackals, peacocks, herons, swans, lions and dogs etc. are all kinds of creatures on this earth belonging to different species. All these creatures are in different forms with different purposes to serve. Everyone cannot become a king. A crow is not meant to reign over a kingdom. Now I shall tell you the story of a heron."

"All right, tell me."

The vulture began narrating the story—

❏ ❏

# 7

# THE SANCTIMONIOUS HERON

There was a pond in Malava country. On the bank of it there lived an old heron. He didn't have to worry for food during his young age, but after becoming old it had become difficult for him to arrange food for himself. With the result he sometimes had to starve for days together.

One day the heron was sitting wearing a sad look on his face. Seeing him sad-stricken a crab asked, "Why, uncle! Why do you look so sad?"

"Oh my son! How to tell you! You also know that I subsist on fish only. But ever since I have heard that some fishermen are coming toward this pond to catch fish, I have been worried about them. This is the reason why I have stopped eating fish."

The crab happily went and informed the fish of the good news that the heron had stopped eating fish and that some fishermen were coming to catch fish from the pond. Hearing this the fish came and said to the heron, "Heron uncle! Please suggest to us some way so that we could save our lives from the cruel hands of the fishermen."

The heron said, "The only way to save your lives is that all of you should be transferred from this pond to some other pond. And for this I can render my services. I can hoist you on my back one by one and take you to some other pond."

The old heron would hoist one fish on his back each time, take him behind a hillock, eat him and then return to take the next one with him. And thus, the wicked heron kept eating his fill for days together. Now he had become healthier. He had become physically fit. One day the crab said to him, "Uncle! I too am bored of living in this pond. Please shift me also from here."

The heron hoisted the crab on his back and took him behind the hillock, where a heap of bones of the fish could be seen very clearly. It took no time for the crab to understand that the wicked heron had eaten away the fish which he had brought one by one under the pretext of shifting them to some other pond, and that now it was his turn to be devoured by him.

The crab caught the heron by his neck with his sharp claws.

"Oh, oh, crab! What are you doing?"

"I am doing only what you have done to the fish of the pond. Now you have been totally exposed. You cheat! You sinner," saying this the crab began piercing his claws deep into the throat of the heron. The heron ultimately died and fell on the heap of the bones of the fish.

"Minister!" said King Mayur after hearing the story from the vulture, "By declaring the crow king of our neighbouring country we shall be able to exercise complete control over it."

"King!" said the vulture, "A person, who becomes happy dreaming about his future, meets the same end, like a Brahmin whose dreams shattered with the breaking of his vessel."

"And what's that story?"

"Listen, I shall tell you the story of that poor Brahmin."

❏ ❏

# 8

# A POOR BRAHMIN'S DREAM

Once a poor Brahmin named Devsharma was passing through a forest.

He had a pitcher full of millet on his head.

He halted in the way and camped for a short period in the house of a potter to take rest. The room in which the potter made him stay was full of vessels made of clay.

The Brahmin thought that the potter must be earning his livelihood by selling these vessels.

He thought—'I too have a pitcher full of millet. I can start my business with this stock. And thus, I shall be able to get rid of my poverty at least. I have to keep wandering from village to village in order to get something to eat. If I could manage to run my business sitting at home my life would become pleasurable.

"Yes, yes, I shall sell away the millet along with the pitcher and shall buy a nanny goat with the money earned from it. Then I shall collect money by selling its milk. Then the goat will give birth to many kids. The goat will give birth to three to four kids every three-four months. And then I shall be having at least twelve male and female kids in a year. I shall earn so much money by selling them that I shall get myself married. I shall bring a beautiful bride. Then the number of goats will multiply which will fetch me so much money that I shall be able to bring one more wife for myself. And in case they ever disobey me I shall beat them with my staff like this—'

Thinking this the Brahmin hit his pitcher with his staff so hard that it broke into pieces and the millet scattered on the floor.

But the Brahmin was still imagining that he was beating his wives with his staff. And in this process he broke many pitchers of the potter also kept in that room.

When the potter saw his pitchers and other earthen pots broken, he became very angry. He beat the Brahmin very badly.

The poor Brahmin, having lost all he had, returned home with tears in his eyes.

And this is the reason why I say that you should stop dreaming about future.

King Mayur said to the vulture, "O minister! Do whatever you deem fit. I know you are very wise. You can never take a wrong decision."

"My final decision is that we should leave the kingdom of

Hiranyagarbha in his care and befriend him. After this we should return to our country as the rainy season is about to begin. Once the rains start it will become difficult for us to return. It's quite possible that Hiranyagarbha, taking advantage of the rainy season, may launch a fresh attack on us. What will happen to us then? Perhaps you have not heard the story of the two demons who, despite being extremely powerful beings of their time, lost their lives because of their foolishness."

"How did that happen?"

"Listen, I am going to narrate their story."

❑ ❑

# 9

# TWO DEMONS

There were two powerful demons, Yudhasunda and Upasunda during ancient times. Even the gods trembled with fear to hear their names. The most powerful of their enemies had succumbed to death during combats with them. This was the reason why people all around had accepted them unanimously as their kings.

Intoxicated with the pride of their power the two brothers thought— 'The earth is of course in our complete possession; now we must take the heavens and the infernal regions also in our possession. And having taken possession of all these three worlds we should attain the status of God.'

And with this aim the two brothers began leading an ascetic life and offering their worships to Lord Shiva.

Pleased with their devotion Lord Shiva appeared to them and said, "O devotees! I am pleased with you two. You may ask for anything you like."

Selfishness had put them on a wrong track owing to which they had lost their mental equilibrium completely. They, instead of asking for possession of the three worlds, said, "O Lord! If you are really kind to us, please give your Parvati Ji to us."

Lord Shiva was extremely infuriated to hear them speak in this manner, but he was helpless; He had given a word. It would not have been proper for him to go back on his word; and so he handed over Parvati Ji to them.

Now Parvati Ji was in the possession of both the brothers. But the problem was that Parvati Ji was one and they were two. The question was that with whom should Parvati Ji go.

They began quarrelling with each other in order to take possession of Parvati Ji. Ultimately, not able to reach an amicable settlement they began looking for someone to intervene and decide the case. They thought that their case could be decided only by a man of wisdom.

So they approached a Brahmin to settle their case. The followers of Lord Shiva were laughing to see that the demons, who were real brothers, were fighting among themselves for a woman. They were ready to quench their thirst with the blood of each other.

The two demons explained their problem to the Brahmin and said, "We leave it to you to decide as to who should have Parvati Ji in his possession."

The Brahmin thought—"These two brothers are fierce demons. Judgement given in favour of any one of the two would infuriate the other one. And in both the cases it will be I who will be the loser. I shall be killed by either of the two. So the Brahmin said, "Look, brothers! You to are brave demons. And I am a Brahmin. I am not capable of giving any judgement. Generally it is the physical might which decides cases among demon clan. So, why don't you two fight a duel with each other? The stronger of the two of you will take Parvati Ji in his possession."

This kind of suggestion suited their temperament and they agreed to decide their case by fighting a duel.

And within no time they were at grips with each other.

Both the demons succumbed to their injuries and died ultimately. Parvati Ji returned to Lord Shiva.

"O king! What I wish to stress upon is that no one benefits from wars. We must make friends with Hiranyagarbha," said the vulture after narrating the story.

King Mayur invited the crow also to express his views. The crow said, "Hiranyagarbha is an innocent king. He trusted me and lost everything as a result. I shall tell you the story of a Brahmin who was also innocent like King Hiranyagarbha."

"Yes, Please go on."

"Listen, O King!" saying this the crow began narrating this story—

❑ ❑

# 10

# AN INNOCENT BRAHMIN

There lived a Brahmin in the hermitage of sage Gautama. Once he performed a Yajna in the house of someone, and the host gave him a nanny goat as a token of reward. The Brahmin set out to the hermitage happily with the goat.

Three cheats, seeing the Brahmin going with a milch goat, thought that they should somehow manage to take away the goat from the simple and innocent Brahmin. But since killing a Brahmin is considered a sin, they decided to manage it cleverly. The three cheats thought of a plan—they stood in the way at some distance from each other.

As soon as the Brahmin reached near the first cheat, he stepped forward and said with folded hands—"Namaskar, Pandit Ji!"

"Namaskar!" replied Pandit Ji with great affection.

"Pandit Ji! From where are you bringing this dog?"

"Dog? No, no, brother! This is a goat."

"Pandit Ji! This of course is a dog, but I don't mind calling it a goat if you so wish."

"Shut up, you wicked man! Don't call my goat a dog," saying this Pandit Ji proceeded toward his destination. There was another cheat in the way waiting for him. He too offered his salutations to Pandit Ji and said, "Pandit Ji! Your dog is indeed very nice."

"No, brother! This is a goat."

"I fail to understand that an erudite scholar like you is calling this dog a goat."

The Brahmin became very angry to hear this, but he didn't say anything and continued moving with his goat. The third cheat was also standing in the way fully prepared to execute his plan. He too offered his salutations to Pandit Ji and said, "Be careful, Pandit JI! See that your dog doesn't bite me."

"Dog...Dog...Dog...Everyone is calling it a dog. Is it that I am making a mistake and carrying a dog home instead of a goat? It seems my host has cheated on me."

Filled with anger the Brahmin left the goat and applying all sorts of contemptuous and abusive epithets to his host, he quickly went away from there. The three cheats took the goat in their possession by cheating the innocent Brahmin.

"King! Sometimes even the most wise ones are fooled by the wicked ones. That's how a camel was also killed."

"How?"

"Listen, please," and the crow began narrating another story.

❏ ❏

# 11

# END OF A POOR CAMEL

There lived a lion named Madotkata in a forest. He had two servants—a crow and a jackal—who used to subsist over the leftovers of the lion. The lion would kill his prey and eat it and the remaining portion would be devoured by his servants.

Once the lion could not kill a prey for two days. With the result the lion, the crow and the jackal remained hungry for two days and kept wandering in the forests in search of prey. Suddenly they saw a camel coming toward the forests. The crow and the jackal became very happy to see him. They went to him and began asking him displaying a great deal of love, "O stranger! How did you happen to come to this place?"

"In fact while grazing with my friends I got disorientated and separated from my friends."

"Brother! Please come with us. We shall take you to the lion who is the king of this forest. He is very kind. He always helps the strangers. He will also tell you which way to go so that you may join your friends again."

The camel, having no alternative, agreed to go and meet the lion. One, in a difficult situation, has to have faith in someone. The camel met the lion and explained to him how he got disorientated. The lion pitied him and said that he could live in the forest fearlessly. He also made friends with the camel. The jackal in fact wanted the lion to kill the camel so that he could have something to eat. But their becoming friendly with each other spoiled the whole game plan.

A jackal's mind is considered a devil's workshop. He was hell-bent to eat the flesh of the camel, no matter what he might have to do for it. The jackal decided that he and the crow wouldn't go in search of prey for the lion. And, when hungry, the lion would automatically kill the camel and eat him. He knew that the lion couldn't devour the whole of the camel all alone; and so they shall have sufficient flesh left for themselves to eat.

Thinking all this the jackal and the crow approached the lion and said, "O king! Look, we have been wandering about in the forests in search of a prey for you for the last three days, but to no avail."

"What shall we eat then?" asked the lion.

"King! If you don't take it otherwise, this camel..."

"No, no, this is impossible and unthinkable. He is our guest and a friend as well. I am a king of this forest; I can't do a base deed like this," said the lion angrily with bloodshot eyes.

"Lord! It is true you are a king; and a king should do what is ethical. But if the camel himself offers his flesh to you to assuage your hunger, you should not decline to accept it," said the crow applying all his cunningness.

The crow had succeeded in hitting the target accurately. The lion agreed to accept the flesh of the camel if offered by him on his own.

There was none as cunning as the crow and the jackal in the forest. They immediately went to the camel and began talking to him in a friendly way, as if they were the only well-wishers of the camel in the entire world.

During their friendly talk the jackal said to the camel, "Look, friend! Our king has had nothing to eat for the last three days, and we cannot allow our king to starve to death. Come, let us go and tell him that since we could not get anything for him to eat during these last three days, we could at least provide our flesh to him to save him from starvation."

The camel said, "Yes, I fully agree with you. It is the duty of the subjects to make any sacrifice for the king when he is in a difficult situation."

All the three went to the lion. First the jackal and the crow said, "O king! You have been starving for the last three days. Please eat us and assuage your hunger."

"No, I cannot eat your flesh. You two are my servants. Above all you don't have sufficient flesh in your bodies."

Realizing that the lion was not prepared to devour the flesh of his servants, the camel offered himself and said, "O king! You may assuage your hunger by eating my flesh."

As if the lion was waiting for the camel to come out with this kind of offer. He immediately pounced on the camel and killed it. He ate his fill and left the remaining portion for the jackal and the crow.

The simple and innocent camel lost his life owing to the wickedness of the jackal and the crow.

"O king! This is the reason why I say that one should not be misguided by someone who is wicked. I remember the story of an old snake who managed to take the frogs in his trap and devoured them."

"And what's that story?"

"Listen, O king!"

❑ ❑

# 12

# A CUNNING SERPENT

There lived a black serpent in the hollow of a Peepal tree along the bank of the river, Ananda.

During his youth he had enjoyed his life thoroughly, but during his old age, owing to his physical infirmity, he was having tough time arranging food for himself. His condition was worsening day by day.

He began thinking that if he continued to starve thus for a few more days he might die a prematured death.

One who starves, also finds some way to assuage his hunger.

The serpent too did the same. Lying by the side of the river he arrived at a conclusion that he shall have to deal tactfully with frogs to arrange his meals.

Next day the serpent went and sat coiled on the bank of the river wearing a very sad look. The king of the frogs came near him and asked, "O king of serpents! What's wrong with you? Why do you look so sad? Please do tell me frankly if there is anything that I could do for you."

"Brother! I don't know how to explain my problem to you. You won't believe me if I tell you the truth, and telling a lie is a sin. I am in a dilemma. I know you cannot trust a serpent."

"O king of serpents! Open your heart to me. I shall believe every word you say if it is worth believing."

"Look, O king of frogs! Once I had killed a Brahmin's son. The Brahmin cursed me that as a measure of punishment I shall have to carry loads of frogs on my back."

The king of frogs became silent to hear the serpent speak thus. Then the serpent said, "I knew you wouldn't believe me. But I have to reap the consequences of the curse laid on me. One thing I can say— if you don't trust me, at least give me a chance to prove my truthfulness. Sit on my back and see for yourself whether I am cheating you or not. Once you develop faith in me you may come everyday to take a ride and I shall take you around. This will at least free me from the influence of curse."

The king of frogs pitied the serpent and agreed to take a ride and go around.

This was for the first time in his life that the king of frogs was riding someone's back. He was enjoying his ride thoroughly. The other creatures of the forest were watching the scene with a little surprise. And this added to the pride of the frog.

Next day, again the serpent came there. He allowed the king of frogs to sit on his back and began moving. But his movements were very slow. The king of frogs inquired, "What's the matter with you, O king of serpents? Why are you moving at such a slow speed?"

"Now how to tell you that I haven't had anything to eat till now. A starving creature moves like this only."

"O king of serpents! You keep serving me like this and I shall allow you to eat one frog everyday."

The serpent became very happy thinking that he had succeeded in his ruse. Now it had become a daily routine for him to take the king of frogs around on his back and eat one frog everyday in return for the service rendered by him. His old age did not bother him any more.

Someone has correctly said that even kings' treasures exhaust if spent extravagantly.

The same thing happened to frogs also. Eating one frog everyday, the serpent made the river devoid of frogs. And finally he devoured the king of frogs also. This was in fact due to the tactfulness of the old serpent that he managed to devour all the frogs of the river.

"This is the reason why I tell you not to declare the crow king of the neighbouring country. I personally feel that we should make friends with Hiranyagarbha and allow him to run his country. A king's friendship suits with a king only."

"How can you say that, minister? Why do you forget that the ethics of politics lays that a defeated enemy should be treated as a slave, and not like a friend."

Just then the messenger of King Mayur came and informed King Mayur that the king of Sinhal island, who was a stork, had launched an attack on their country.

Then the vulture said to his king, "O king! We shall have to return to our country at once. It seems the stork has launched an attack taking advantage of the present circumstances. Now we must strike a compromise deal with Hiranyagarbha. And the advantage of this compromise deal will be that Hiranyagarbha will help us fight and counter the attack of the enemy king, stork."

King Mayur said, "I think we must follow the advice of the vulture. We should befriend Hiranyagarbha."

Just then the vulture called on Hiranyagarbha and struck a compromise with him. King Mayur and Hiranyagarbha became friends.

Both the kings joined hands against the army of King Stork and defeated him. But this was in fact the victory of knowledge of politics which was rendered by the vulture.

Having narrated the stories of 'Compromise,' Vishnu Sharma said, "Now tell me, what more shall I tell you."

The princes said, "Gurudev! You have kindly taught us the ethics of our royal duties. Not only that we have enjoyed the stories, we have also improved our knowledge."

Hearing this Vishnu Sharma said, "May all the kings remain friendly with victorious kings. May there be happiness all around. May the noble ones enjoy every happiness. May the erudite scholars attain name and fame. Let there be happiness all around. Let us wish that Lakshmi Ji resides permanently in the heart of Lord Vishnu so long as Lord Shiva and Parvati Ji exist. And so long as the heavens and earth remain in existence, may this collection of stories render benefits to humankind.

❏ ❏ ❏